LOGIC DESIGN WITH INTEGRATED CIRCUITS

Logic Design with
Integrated Circuits

WILLIAM E. WICKES

Senior Staff Engineer
Hughes Aircraft Company

JOHN WILEY & SONS, INC.

New York · London · Sydney

Dedicated to my loving wife, DEE

PREFACE

Digital equipment is characterized by the use of logic building blocks such as gates, flip-flops, registers, adders, and accumulators. Hundreds and thousands of these building blocks can be required in a given complex digital apparatus. Microelectronics has reduced their size to a point at which they can be used by the hundreds and thousands without requiring cabinets of space. Logic building blocks have truly become a component. One, two, four, eight, and more flip-flops as well as complete functional units, such as adders, registers, and memories, are available in a package no larger than a single transistor. The microelectronic digital IC (integrated circuit) provides a new family of components by which digital techniques can be used to solve complex problems with greater reliability, lower cost, and smaller volume than could ever be hoped for with discrete components.

Digital techniques have long been available as a design tool, but not until microelectronics could these techniques be fully exploited. Management no longer questions whether to go "micro" or not in the design of new digital equipment; it would be economic suicide not to. The low cost, small size, and reliability of digital ICs have resulted in the use of special-purpose digital techniques to perform more and more functions, and the applications engineer is being pushed to provide digital solutions to the system problems.

This book is written for the applications engineer who is struggling to stay abreast of the "state of the art." It brings together the analytical and empirical tools necessary to design with digital ICs. Some of the material is thought to be original, but with the vast amount of energy being applied to this field it is difficult to be sure. The book is intended to be used to teach the basics of logic design, provide insight into the applications of digital techniques, and serve as a reference text for advanced thinking. Fabrication of integrated circuits is progressing at such a phenomenal rate that lack of knowledge is this field has already become a handicap to the engineer. Special-purpose, hard-wired computer techniques are being applied in every major military and space program. The need to understand and use these techniques encompasses personnel from the junior technician to top-level management.

This book is not intended to provide a complete or rigorous theoretical introduction to logic design. It is written for the engineer who wants to use digital integrated circuits in the design of digital equipment. It contains, therefore, only that information felt necessary to become proficient in this relatively new art. The subject matter is chosen from actual experience and has been used to teach practicing technicians, engineers, and managers. The sequence of the material results in a building-block approach whereby one chapter leads to the next and procedures learned in one section are applied and expanded in the following sections. No pre-requisites are required because all mathematics and techniques are developed.

The basic tools of the logic designer are presented in Chapters 1, 2, and 3 as number systems, Boolean algebra, and minimization aids. Thorough understanding of these fundamentals will serve as a foundation for the remaining material. The binary number system is obviously necessary for a comprehension of digital logic design and so the reader is first exposed to the fundamentals of number systems and a few number codes used in digital equipment. The chapter on Boolean algebra is reduced to a minimum because much material is already available. This is not intended to imply that algebra is not necessary (it is the backbone of all logic design) but rather that a minimal amount is all that is required to get started. More detailed development of the algebra and its theorems can be found in references in the bibliography. Minimization aids are important for understanding the material to follow. The reader may well want to expand his capabilities with the various techniques such as mapping, numerical assignments, and computer analysis. Ability to understand and apply minimization cannot be overstressed.

Chapter 4, "Digital Integrated Circuits," provides a brief history of the evolution of digital integrated circuits and the association of some of the currently available digital circuits with one of four fundamental logic types. The objective is to provide insight into the actual circuit types being used by the manufacturers of digital ICs and reduce the seemingly vast variety of ICs to a realm of comprehension. This chapter has provoked considerable thought about exactly where it should be located in the book and to what depth the discussion should go on characteristics of logic available now and in the future. In teaching this material I have found it desirable to acquaint the student with hardware to be used in logic design before actually making any design. This helps in the visualization of actual hardware count during the design process. No detailed dissertation on all the logic types presently manufactured, however, is provided or felt necessary, because the actual components are changing too rapidly. The detailed hardware used to build actual equipment can range from one flip-flop to a complex 100-bit shift register in a single package. In the one case the logic designer needs to implement the shift register with individual flip-flops, whereas in the other he need only know its logic characteristics as a single-functional unit.

Chapter 5, "Combinational Logic," presents the basic techniques related to switching functions. Extensive treatment of AND and OR gates by examples provides insight into the anlysis and implementation of Boolean algebraic equations. The more modern techniques of implementing with NAND and NOR gates follows, because integrated circuit building blocks are predominantly of this type. The techniques developed in this chapter are expanded and utilized throughout the rest of the book.

An introduction to and the fundamental theories of sequential logic are presented in Chapter 6, "Sequential Networks." Combinational logic deals with functions that respond to the state of the input signals. Sequential logic requires a knowledge of what the sequence of inputs has been as well as what they are at any particular moment. Chapter 7, "Pulsed Sequential Networks," applies the theories of sequential networks to flip-flop applications by introducing the concept of the state diagram. The ultimate objective of sequential logic in Chapter 6 is to minimize the memory with strictly NAND or NOR gates and was originally conceived to minimize the number of relays required. ICs, however, have made the cost of a flip-flop not much greater than that of a logic gate; therefore pulsed sequential techniques exploit the flip-flop as the memory element.

Chapter 8, "Flip-Flop Programming," defines the various types of flip-flop available and applies the techniques of Chapter 7 to illustrate programming relationships among them. There is also a section devoted to simplifying the analytical techniques developed in Chapter 7 on flip-flop networks.

Although Chapters 7 and 8 deal with flip-flops as general-purpose programming devices, Chapter 9, "Flip-Flop Counters," concentrates on the flip-flop used in counters. All the basic types of counter are described and explained, as well as many special-purpose applications. The last section in Chapter 9 implements counters for all counts from 2 through 16 by utilizing the popular, general-purpose J-K flip-flop.

Chapter 10, "Special-Purpose Functions," deals with two techniques that have just begun to be exploited: the discrete multiplier and the digital differential analyzer. There are examples to illustrate the techniques, and it is left to the student to expand their applications.

I am indebted to many friends who have contributed directly and indirectly to the preparation of this material; in particular Donald F. Perkins for his ideas, Lee Friedline for her typing, R. D. Hudson, Jr., and R. F. Shea for their encouragement, and my wife Dee for her patience and devotion.

William E. Wickes

Manhattan Beach, California
March 1968

CONTENTS

LOGIC DESIGN WITH INTEGRATED CIRCUITS

1

NUMBER SYSTEMS

1.1 INTRODUCTION

The number system utilized for every-day transactions is the decimal number system. This system has become so commonplace that the average person has forgotten it is a unique and discrete number system selected from an infinite variety of possible systems.

The number 5673, for example, represents five thousand, six hundred, seventy, and three in the decimal system and is composed of the digits 5, 6, 7, and 3. The decimal system makes use of the 10 digits 0, 1, 2, 3, 4, 5, 6, 7, 8, and 9 to represent numbers and uses powers of 10 for numbers above 9. That is, the number 5673 represents the sum of 5000 (5×10^3) plus 600 (6×10^2) plus 70 (7×10^1) plus 3 (3×10^0). A number system such as this is said to be based on a *radix* of 10. In a number system with a base or radix r the digits used are from 0 to $r - 1$. Thus the decimal number system with a base of 10 requires digits from 0 to $r - 1$, or 9. The number can be expressed mathematically as

$$N = a_0 r^0 + a_1 r^1 + a_2 r^2 + \cdots + a_n r^n,$$

where $n = 0, 1, 2, 3, \cdots \infty$

$r = $ base or radix of number system

$a = $ number digits having values between 0 and $r - 1$.

The above equation is valid for $N \geq 1$. For $0 < N < 1$ the following equation holds:

$$N = a_{-1} r^{-1} + a_{-2} r^{-2} + a_{-3} r^{-3} + \cdots + a_{-n} r^{-n}.$$

1

TABLE 1.1 Conversion Table

Decimal (10)	Octal (8)	Binary (2)
0	0	0
1	1	1
2	2	10
3	3	11
4	4	100
5	5	101
6	6	110
7	7	111
8	10	1000
9	11	1001
10	12	1010
11	13	1011
12	14	1100
13	15	1101
14	16	1110
15	17	1111
16	20	10000
17	21	10001
18	22	10010
19	23	10011
20	24	10100
21	25	10101
22	26	10110
23	27	10111
24	30	11000
25	31	11001
26	32	11010
27	33	11011
28	34	11100
29	35	11101
30	36	11110
31	37	11111
32	40	100000
.	.	.
.	.	.
.	.	.
64	100	1000000

Thus for the integer 5673

$$N = 5673$$

$$= 3 + 70 + 600 + 5000$$

$$= 3 \times 10^0 + 7 \times 10^1 + a_2 \times 10^2 + a_3 \times 10^3$$

$$= a_0 \times 10^0 + a_1 \times 10^1 + a_2 \times 10^2 + a_3 \times 10^3,$$

where $a_0 = 3$,

$\quad\quad a_1 = 7$,

$\quad\quad a_2 = 6$,

$\quad\quad a_3 = 5$.

In general numbers are written with the least significant digit on the right and the most significant digit on the left.

1.2   OCTAL NUMBER SYSTEM

A number system useful in computer technology is the octal number system, which uses a base or radix of 8. From the previous definitions the useful digits in an octal system are the digits from 0 to $r - 1$, or $8 - 1$ or 7. Thus the symbols for 8 and 9 are not used and are meaningless in an octal system. The only digits required are 0, 1, 2, 3, 4, 5, 6, and 7.

The number 265 in the octal system, therefore, means

$$N = 265_{(8)}$$
$$= 5 \times 8^0 + 6 \times 8^1 + 2 \times 8^2.$$

Table 1.1 illustrates the relationship between decimal and octal numbers from 0 through 32. Notice that octal 7 is followed by octal 10 in the same manner that decimal 9 is followed by decimal 10. Octal 10 represents 0×8^0 plus 1×8^1 and is not to be confused with decimal 10, which represents 0×10^0 plus 1×10^1.

There are several techniques for conversion from a decimal number to an octal number. One such method is successive division. That is, to convert a decimal number to an octal number, successively divide the number by the base 8. This can be best illustrated by an example.

EXAMPLE 1.1. *Find the octal equivalent of the decimal number 673.*

$$\frac{673}{8} = 84 + 1,$$

$$\frac{84}{8} = 10 + 4,$$

$$\frac{10}{8} = 1 + 2,$$

$$\frac{1}{8} = 0 + 1.$$

Therefore $673_{(10)} = 1241_{(8)}$.

This procedure can be expressed mathematically as

$$\frac{N}{r} = b + a_0,$$

$$\frac{b}{r} = c + a_1,$$

$$\frac{c}{r} = d + a_2,$$

$$\vdots$$

and $N_{(r)} = a_n \ldots a_2 a_1 a_0.$

Notice that the first remainder is the least significant digit and the last remainder obtained is the most significant digit.

EXAMPLE 1.2. *Find the octal equivalent of the decimal number 512.*

$$\frac{512}{8} = 64 + 0,$$

$$\frac{64}{8} = 8 + 0,$$

$$\frac{8}{8} = 1 + 0,$$

$$\frac{1}{8} = 0 + 1,$$

giving $512_{(10)} = 1000_{(8)}.$

This is verified by Table 1.2, where $8^3 = 512_{(10)}.$

The power table, Table 1.2, is useful when converting from an octal number to a decimal number. The individual digits are multiplied by the appropriate power of 8 and then added. That is, to convert the octal number 1241 to a decimal number requires the application of the power equation

$$N_{(10)} = a_0 r^0 + a_1 r^1 + a_2 r^2 + a_3 r^3$$
$$= 1 \times 8^0 + 4 \times 8^1 + 2 + 8^2 + 1 \times 8^3$$
$$= 1 \times 1 + 4 \times 8 + 2 \times 64 + 1 \times 512$$
$$= 1 + 32 + 128 + 512$$
$$= 673.$$

Thus $1241_{(8)} = 673_{(10)}$ and verifies the correctness of our earlier example.

TABLE 1.2 Power Table

N	Decimal (10)	Octal (8)	Binary (2) (+)	Binary (2) (−)
0	1	1	1	1.0
1	10	8	2	0.5
2	100	64	4	0.25
3	1,000	512	8	0.125
4	10,000	4,096	16	0.0625
5	100,000	32,768	32	0.03125
6	1,000,000	262,114	64	0.015625
7	10,000,000	2,096,912	128	0.0078125
8	.	.	256	0.00390625
9	.	.	512	0.001953125
10	.	.	1,024	0.0009765625

EXAMPLE 1.3. *Convert* $2671_{(8)}$ *to its decimal equivalent.*

$$N_{(10)} = 1 \times 8^0 + 7 \times 8^1 + 6 \times 8^2 + 2 \times 8^3$$
$$= 1 \times 1 + 7 \times 8 + 6 \times 64 + 2 \times 512$$
$$= 1 + 56 + 384 + 1024$$
$$= 1465.$$

Thus $2671_{(8)} = 1465_{(10)}$.

It is left to the reader to prove the correctness of this example by converting $1465_{(10)}$ to its octal equivalent.

1.3 BINARY NUMBER SYSTEM

The binary number system has a base of 2. Because $r = 2$, only 2 digits are required and these are from 0 to $r - 1$, or $2 - 1$ or 1. Thus only the number digits 0 and 1 are required to express numbers in the binary number system. Also, from previous definitions, it can be seen that the binary number 10111 means

$$N = 10111_{(2)}$$
$$= 1 \times 2^0 + 1 \times 2^1 + 1 \times 2^2 + 0 \times 2^3 + 1 \times 2^4$$
$$= 1 + 2 + 4 + 0 + 16$$
$$= 23_{(10)}.$$

The design of switching networks was greatly enhanced by the application of binary mathematics. Switching networks were defined as having only two possible states: closed or open. This led to great strides in analyzing and simplifying complex switching operations, with obvious extensions into digital computers.

The binary number system follows the same rules given for the octal and decimal systems. Conversion of a decimal number to a binary number can be accomplished by successive division by the base number 2.

EXAMPLE 1.4. *Convert $356_{(10)}$ to a binary number.*

$$\frac{356}{2} = 178 + 0,$$

$$\frac{178}{2} = 89 + 0,$$

$$\frac{89}{2} = 44 + 1,$$

$$\frac{44}{2} = 22 + 0,$$

$$\frac{22}{2} = 11 + 0,$$

$$\frac{11}{2} = 5 + 1,$$

$$\frac{5}{2} = 2 + 1,$$

$$\frac{2}{2} = 1 + 0,$$

$$\frac{1}{2} = 0 + 1,$$

giving $356_{(10)} = 101100100_{(2)}$.

It can be seen that a binary system is not economical of number digits. That is, it takes nine number digits (101100100) in base 2 to express what three number digits (356) do in the base 10. The decimal number also is much easier to converse with and remember than a binary number. Thus, whereas a binary number is nice for two-state functions, a decimal number is more convenient for the human to handle and communicate.

EXAMPLE 1.5. *Find the binary equivalent of the decimal 55.*

$$\frac{55}{2} = 27 + 1,$$

$$\frac{27}{2} = 13 + 1,$$

$$\frac{13}{2} = 6 + 1,$$

$$\frac{6}{2} = 3 + 0,$$

$$\frac{3}{2} = 1 + 1,$$

$$\frac{1}{2} = 0 + 1,$$

giving $55_{(10)} = 110111_{(2)}$.

The reverse process, converting a binary number to its decimal equivalent, is accomplished using Table 1.2. This time, however, each power of 2 is multiplied by either 1 or 0, depending on the number digit. This results in a simple addition of the appropriate power of 2, as can be seen from the following example.

EXAMPLE 1.6. *Convert $100110_{(2)}$ to its decimal equivalent.*

$$N = 100110_{(2)}$$
$$= 0 \times 2^0 + 1 \times 2^1 + 1 \times 2^2 + 0 \times 2^3 + 0 \times 2^4 + 1 \times 2^5$$
$$= 0 + 2 + 4 + 0 + 0 + 32$$
$$= 38_{(10)}.$$

The conversion of the binary number 100001 to its decimal equivalent is thus accomplished by the simple addition of 2^0 and 2^5, which from Table 1.2 are 1 and 32, giving the decimal number 33. Then

$$100001_{(2)} = 33_{(10)}.$$

Decimal fractions are converted by a slightly different process than the whole numbers. The decimal fraction number is repeatedly multiplied by the base number and the carry (or overflow) is recorded. This can be illustrated by the following examples.

EXAMPLE 1.7. *Convert* $0.6875_{(10)}$ *to a binary number.*

$$0.6875$$
$$\times 2$$

$$a_{-1} = \quad 1 \quad 0.3750$$
$$\times 2$$

$$a_{-2} = \quad 0 \quad 0.7500$$
$$\times 2$$

$$a_{-3} = \quad 1 \quad 0.5000$$
$$\times 2$$

$$a_{-4} = \quad 1 \quad 0.0000,$$

giving $0.6875_{(10)} = 0.1011_{(2)}$.

This multiplication process is continued until the decimal number is exhausted, as in the above example, or the desired accuracy is obtained.

EXAMPLE 1.8. *Find the binary equivalent of the decimal 0.56.*

$$0.56$$
$$\times 2$$

$$a_{-1} = \quad 1 \quad 0.12$$
$$\times 2$$

$$a_{-2} = \quad 0 \quad 0.24$$
$$\times 2$$

$$a_{-3} = \quad 0 \quad 0.48$$
$$\times 2$$

$$a_{-4} = \quad 0 \quad 0.96$$
$$\times 2$$

$$a_{-5} = \quad 1 \quad 0.92$$
$$\times 2$$

$$a_{-6} = \quad 1 \quad 0.84$$
$$\times 2$$

$$a_{-7} = \quad 1 \quad 0.68$$
$$\times 2$$

$$a_{-8} = \quad 1 \quad 0.36$$
$$\times 2$$
$$\overline{}$$
$$a_{-9} = \quad 0 \quad 0.72$$
$$\times 2$$
$$\overline{}$$
$$a_{-10} = \quad 1 \quad 0.44,$$
$$\vdots$$

giving $\quad 0.56_{(10)} = 0.1000111101 \ldots_{(2)}$.

This is the same as the decimal fraction $\frac{1}{3}$, which cannot be expressed as a finite number but must be approximated as a decimal number with a finite number of digits.

The conversion of a decimal integer and fractional number is accomplished by separate conversions of each part. That is, the conversion of the whole number is done in one operation while the conversion of the decimal part of the number is accomplished in a separate operation. This can be best illustrated with an example.

EXAMPLE 1.9. *Convert 12.3125 into its binary equivalent.*

Conversion of 12:

$$\frac{12}{2} = 6 + 0,$$

$$\frac{6}{2} = 3 + 0,$$

$$\frac{3}{2} = 1 + 1,$$

$$\frac{1}{2} = 0 + 1,$$

giving $\quad 12_{(10)} = 1100_{(2)}$.

Conversion of 0.3125:

$$0.3125$$
$$\times 2$$
$$\overline{}$$
$$0 \quad 0.6250$$
$$\times 2$$
$$\overline{}$$
$$1 \quad 0.2500$$
$$\times 2$$
$$\overline{}$$

$$0 \quad 0.5000$$
$$\times 2$$
$$\overline{}$$
$$1 \quad 0.0000,$$

giving $0.3125_{(10)} = 0.0101_{(2)}$.

The results above are now combined to form the complete conversion. Thus $12.3125_{(10)} = 1100.0101_{(2)}$.

A useful relationship exists between octal numbers and binary numbers. Octal numbers use the digits 0 through 7. Three binary digits count to a magnitude of 7. That is, the decimal equivalent of binary 111 is decimal 7. If an octal number is taken digit by digit, a 3-digit binary number can be written for each octal digit. The resulting binary number will be a true binary number, which may then be converted to decimal if desired. As an example, the conversion of $236_{(8)}$ will be shown. Note that the octal numbers 0 through 7 are equal to the decimal numbers 0 through 7. It is only above 7 that a difference between the octal and the decimal system occurs.

EXAMPLE 1.10. *Convert $236_{(8)}$ to a binary number.*

The conversion is done digit by digit as though each were an individual number. That is, the 3-digit binary equivalent of the decimal number 6 is 110, which is also the binary equivalent of the octal number 6. The 3-digit binary equivalent of 3 (either decimal 3 or octal 3) is 011, and the 3-digit binary equivalent of 2 is 010. Grouping these in their proper sequence gives

$$236_{(8)} = 010 \quad\quad 011 \quad\quad 110$$
$$= 10011110_{(2)}.$$

The most significant "0" is dropped because it is meaningless, just as $0236_{(10)}$ is the same as $236_{(10)}$.

Converting from binary to octal is just as easy by starting with the least significant bit and converting in groups of three. That is, $10110101_{(2)}$ is equal to $265_{(8)}$ as shown in detail below.

$$010 \quad\quad 110 \quad\quad 101$$
$$2 \quad\quad\quad 6 \quad\quad\quad 5$$

An extra zero had to be added to complete the groupings of three so that the proper magnitude could be obtained.

Because octal numbers make use of 8 digits and are similar to decimal numbers, they are convenient to deal with and are quite useful in programming. They can be converted to binary and back again by inspection and, as noted before, the number 265 is a much simpler number to deal with than 10110101. Some special-purpose numerical displays also make use of this characteristic by directly displaying octal numbers instead of having to resort to BCD (binary-coded decimal) codes and doing binary-to-decimal decoding.

EXAMPLE 1.11. *Convert* $369_{(10)}$ *to octal and then to binary.*

Decimal to octal conversion:

$$\frac{369}{8} = 46 + 1,$$

$$\frac{46}{8} = 5 + 6,$$

$$\frac{5}{8} = 0 + 5.$$

Thus $N_{(10)} = 369$
$N_{(8)} = 561$
$N_{(2)} = 101110001.$

1.4 NUMBER CODES

Binary Code

A code is a systematic way of representing information. It is possible to represent 2^n different messages in a purely binary code of n bits. The binary code is a straightforward direct conversion of the decimal number to the

TABLE 1.3 Truth Table

Decimal	Binary
0	0000
1	0001
2	0010
3	0011
4	0100
5	0101
6	0110
7	0111
8	1000
.	. ↑
.	. └LSB
.	.

binary. This is shown in Table 1.1; it is the most common code used in digital equipment because it is a systematic arrangement of the digits, is a weighted code (where each column has a magnitude of 2^n associated with it), and is easy to translate. In the truth table (Table 1.3) note that the least significant bit (LSB) alternates every time, whereas the second least significant bit repeats every two times, the third least significant bit repeats every four times, and so on.

BCD Code

The next most common code is the BCD (binary-coded decimal) code. The need for a code for each of the 10 decimal digits, 0 through 9, arises often, and there is a large variety of codes from which to choose. The most popular code is the ordinary binary equivalent of the decimal digits as shown in Table 1.4.

TABLE 1.4

Decimal	BCD 8—4—2—1			
0	0	0	0	0
1	0	0	0	1
2	0	0	1	0
3	0	0	1	1
4	0	1	0	0
5	0	1	0	1
6	0	1	1	0
7	0	1	1	1
8	1	0	0	0
9	1	0	0	1
	1	0	1	0
	1	0	1	1
	1	1	0	0
	1	1	0	1
	1	1	1	0
	1	1	1	1

Because 10 digits are involved the minimum number of binary bits required must be sufficient to contain at least 10 different combinations or arrangements of the binary digits. Three bits provide only 2^3 or 8 different combinations. Four bits provide 2^4 or 16 different combinations. The BCD code makes use of the first 10 combinations of the 4-bit function. This provides a weighted code in which the least significant bit has the weight of 2^0 or 1, the next bit has a weight of 2^1 or 2, the third bit has the weight of 2^2 or 4, and the most significant bit has the weight of 2^3 or 8. Thus the decimal equivalent of the binary code is determined by the presence of 1's.

The BCD code provides a 4-bit binary-to-decimal conversion in a manner similar to the 3-bit binary-to-octal conversion. For example, the binary equivalent (in BCD code) of the decimal number 369 is

$$3 \qquad 6 \qquad 9$$
$$0011 \qquad 0110 \qquad 1001,$$
$$\text{giving} \quad 369_{(10)} = 001101101001_{(BCD)}.$$

The conversion of a binary BCD number to its decimal equivalent is done in the reverse manner, as illustrated by the following:

Convert $1001001100100111_{(BCD)} = ?_{(10)}$.

$$1001 \qquad 0011 \qquad 0010 \qquad 0111$$
$$9 \qquad 3 \qquad 2 \qquad 7,$$
$$\text{giving} \quad 9327_{(10)}.$$

Excess-3 Code

Whereas the BCD code makes use of the first 10 of the 16 different combinations of 4 bits, the excess-3 code adds 3 to the decimal number and then converts to binary as shown in Table 1.5. This code is called a non-weighted code because the binary 1's do not represent decimal values.

TABLE 1.5

Decimal	Excess-3			
	0	0	0	0
	0	0	0	1
	0	0	1	0
0	0	0	1	1
1	0	1	0	0
2	0	1	0	1
3	0	1	1	0
4	0	1	1	1
5	1	0	0	0
6	1	0	0	1
7	1	0	1	0
8	1	0	1	1
9	1	1	0	0
	1	1	0	1
	1	1	1	0
	1	1	1	1

The advantage of this type of code is that at least one 1 is present in all states, providing an error-detection ability.

Other Decimal Codes

Many other weighted and nonweighted 4-bit (and more) decimal codes are in use that may have advantages for special implementation problems.

TABLE 1.6

Decimal	8—4—2—1	6—3—1—1	5—2—1—1	5—1—1—1—1	Nonweighted
0	0 0 0 0	0 0 0 0	0 0 0 0	0 0 0 0 0	0 0 0 0 0
1	0 0 0 1	0 0 0 1	0 0 0 1	0 0 0 0 1	0 0 0 0 1
2	0 0 1 0	0 0 1 1	0 1 0 0	0 0 0 1 1	0 0 0 1 1
3	0 0 1 1	0 1 0 0	0 1 1 0	0 0 1 1 1	0 0 1 1 1
4	0 1 0 0	0 1 0 1	0 1 1 1	0 1 1 1 1	0 1 1 1 1
5	0 1 0 1	0 1 1 1	1 0 0 0	1 0 0 0 0	1 1 1 1 1
6	0 1 1 0	1 0 0 0	1 0 0 1	1 1 0 0 0	1 1 1 1 0
7	0 1 1 1	1 0 0 1	1 1 0 0	1 1 1 0 0	1 1 1 0 0
8	1 0 0 0	1 0 1 1	1 1 1 0	1 1 1 1 0	1 1 0 0 0
9	1 0 0 1	1 1 0 0	1 1 1 1	1 1 1 1 1	1 0 0 0 0

The nonweighted decimal code illustrated in Table 1.6 is easy to implement with shift register techniques and can often result in reduced hardware.

Gray Code

Cyclic codes provide the unique property of only a single bit change when going from one state to the next. These codes are also reflective in nature; that is, the lower-order bit sequence is the same when starting from the middle of the count and progressing in either direction.

The Gray code is the most common cyclic code and is illustrated in 4 bits in Table 1.7. This code is developed by starting with the least significant bit and writing the sequence 0110011 .... The next-higher-order bit starts off by two 0's followed by four 1's as 00111100001111 .... The third bit starts off with four 0's followed by alternating groups of eight 1's and eight 0's. This process continues for as many bits as are required until the most significant bit is reached. This bit is a 0 for the first complete half count and a 1 for the remaining half of the combinations. This code was developed for shaft encoders, which are electromechanical devices and need a code that changes only 1 bit from one state to the next in order to avoid ambiguity.

A decimal number can be converted to the Gray code by first converting to the binary code. The binary code is converted to the Gray code by comparing each digit (starting with the least significant digit) with its adjacent

TABLE 1.7 4-Bit Gray Code

0	0	0	0
0	0	0	1
0	0	1	1
0	0	1	0
0	1	1	0
0	1	1	1
0	1	0	1
0	1	0	0
1	1	0	0
1	1	0	1
1	1	1	1
1	1	1	0
1	0	1	0
1	0	1	1
1	0	0	1
1	0	0	0

Reflected

digit. If the two digits being compared are alike (are both 1's or both 0's) the Gray code digit is 0. If the two digits being compared are not alike the Gray code digit is 1. This comparison is the output from an exclusive-OR circuit and can also be referred to as performing a sum modulo 2 comparison. This process of comparison continues for each pair. If there is an even number of binary digits in the word, a 0 must be added in the front of the most significant digit in order to give it a comparison pair.

EXAMPLE 1.12. *Convert $43_{(10)}$ to Gray code.*

$$43_{(10)} = 101011_{(2)}$$

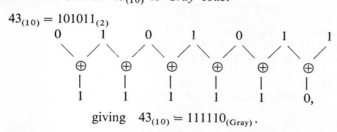

giving $43_{(10)} = 111110_{(Gray)}$.

Converting the Gray code to its decimal equivalent follows the above sequence in reverse. That is, the Gray code is converted to binary and the resulting binary code is then converted to decimal. The conversion of Gray to binary starts with the most significant bit and works down. The high order bits are unchanged until the first 1 is *passed*. This is followed by listing 1's until the next 1 is *met*, followed by 0's until the next 1 is met, and so on. This process continues until the number is exhausted.

As an example, convert $111110_{(Gray)}$ to binary. The conversion to binary is as follows:

1. List high-order bits until the first 1 is passed   1.
2. List 1's until the next 1 is met   −.
3. List 0's until the next 1 is met   0.
4. List 1's until the next 1 is met   1.
   And so on.

Gray code	Binary
1 – – – – –	1
1 1 – – – –	0
1 1 1 – – –	1
1 1 1 1 – –	0
1 1 1 1 1 –	1
1 1 1 1 1 0	1

Thus $111110_{(Gray)} = 101011_{(binary)}$.

PROBLEMS

1. Convert from the decimal number system to the binary number system:

    (a) 23   (g) 47
    (b) 126   (h) 63.25
    (c) 256   (i) 27.0625
    (d) 0.5703 (carry to 12 places)   (j) 113.5
    (e) 10.188 (carry to 12 places)   (k) 73.125
    (f) $\pi/4$ (carry to 12 places) $(\pi = 3.14159)$

2. Convert from the binary number system to the octal number system:

    (a) 110110   (g) 1000101
    (b) 101110   (h) 101010
    (c) 11011111   (i) 011001100
    (d) 101101111   (j) 100001100
    (e) 111101   (k) 111111000
    (f) 110111

3. Convert from the octal number system to the binary number system:

    (a) 725   (g) 673
    (b) 26   (h) 3
    (c) 263   (i) 275
    (d) 5173   (j) 524
    (e) 31   (k) 1023
    (f) 112

4. Convert to binary from decimal, add in binary, and then convert back to the decimal number system:

    (a) $8 + 22$ (d) $35 + 63$
    (b) $31 + 16$ (e) $12 + 69$
    (c) $6 + 24$ (f) $73 + 21$

2

BOOLEAN ALGEBRA

2.1 INTRODUCTION

This book is not intended to provide rigorous mathematical proof of the classic material, but rather to be a summary and reference of those items of normal usage to the applications engineer. There are many excellent sources for these proofs, some of which are contained in the bibliography, for readers who desire to study in greater depth.

Let it be sufficient to note that George Boole (1815–64) introduced an algebra of logic in the mid-1800s that became known as Boolean algebra. However, the present-day application of Boolean algebra to binary functions is credited to a paper by C. E. Shannon in 1938.

The entire framework of the calculus of propositions depends on the concept that logical statements can be made that can be designated as true or false. No assignment of intermediate values is allowed. For example, it can be said about a light switch that it is on or it is off. The lamp in the socket is on or off. This two-valued world leads to the assignment of a 1 if true, or a 0 if false. The numerical representation of statements of logic leads one to algebraic analysis of these statements.

The algebra of logic, calculus of propositions, or Boolean algebra has become the workhorse of the logic designer. However, the application of this mathematics to switching and digital design is still relatively new and much remains to be done. The techniques presented herein are intended to provide as formal an approach to practical problems as possible, but it should be recognized that there is still more art than science in the application of Boolean algebra to digital problems.

2.2 FUNDAMENTALS

The fundamentals of logic design are based on a set of postulates and resulting theorems.

Postulate 1a $X = 1$ if $X \neq 0$.

Postulate 1b $X = 0$ if $X \neq 1$.

These two postulates form the fundamental definition of a dual-valued variable; that is, if the function X is 1, then it cannot be 0; similarly, if it is 0, it cannot be 1. This concurs with the concept of true and false.

Postulate 2a $0 \cdot 0 = 0$.

Postulate 2b $1 + 1 = 1$.

These postulates introduce the notations " $\cdot$ " and " $+$." It is assumed the " $=$ " symbol will be accepted in its conventional sense of equality. The " $\cdot$ " symbol implies multiplication in ordinary algebra but here will imply the logical AND. Postulate 2a is read 0 AND 0 equals 0. The " $+$ " symbol does not mean addition, but rather the logical OR function. Thus Postulate 2b is read as 1 OR 1 equals 1. It will become apparent that the " $\cdot$ " and " $+$ " will have characteristics identical with those of ordinary algebra with the one exception above, where $1 + 1 = 1$.

Postulate 2b is the dual of 2a just as postulate 1b is the dual of 1a. This duality is defined as the exchanging of all " $\cdot$ " to " $+$," all " $+$ " to " $\cdot$," all 1's to 0's, and all 0's to 1's. This principle of duality is apparent with the postulates and theorems of Boolean algebra.

Postulate 3a $1 \cdot 1 = 1$.

Postulate 3b $0 + 0 = 0$.

Postulate 4a $1 \cdot 0 = 0 \cdot 1 = 0$.

Postulate 4b $0 + 1 = 1 + 0 = 1$.

Postulate 5a $\bar{0} = 1$.

Postulate 5b $\bar{1} = 0$.

Postulate 3a conveys the concept that 1 AND 1 is still equal to 1 while Postulate 3b, the dual, introduces the notion of 0 OR 0 is still equal to 0.

Postulates 4a and 4b, while basic in appearance, are very powerful in binary manipulation. The idea is similar to ordinary algebra in that 1 AND 0 (1 multiplied by 0) is 0 while 1 OR 0 (1 added to 0) is 1. These also demonstrate that the commutative laws of ordinary algebra also apply to Boolean algebra.

Postulates 5a and 5b present the notion of a complement function. That is, the complement of 1 is 0 and the complement of 0 is 1. This has also been called the negation, negative, or NOT postulate.

These postulates form the basis for all the theorems in Boolean algebra.

2.3   THEOREMS

As in ordinary algebra the letters of the alphabet are used to represent variables, the distinction being that Boolean variables may only have the value 1; and if not 1, then 0. We can define the transistor switch as being in the full ON state or the full OFF state. If we assign the digit 1 to the full ON state, then we must assign the digit 0 to the full OFF state. We can talk about switch A as being ON or OFF, or in the 1 state or the 0 state. This agrees with the calculus of propositions, whereby the digits 1 and 0 do not represent numerical values, but rather states or conditions. If transistor switch A is on, we can say $A = 1$. If switch A is off, we can say $A = 0$. Notice that both states cannot exist simultaneously, but rather are finite. If we assume the definition $A = 1$, then we are implying $\bar{A} = 0$ from Postulate 5b. But if we assume the definition $A = 0$, then we must accept the fact $\bar{A} = 1$ from Postulate 5a. Either is correct by itself but both conflict when jointly applied. The application of this algebra must then be supported by proper definitions of the variables and their assumed states.

The occurrence of " $\cdot$ " is often omitted as a convenience. Thus the expression

$$A \cdot B + C$$

can appear as

$$AB + C.$$

Theorem 1a $X + 0 = X.$

Theorem 1b $X \cdot 1 = X.$

The "$+$" symbol reads as OR and can be related to a parallel connection of two switches or groups of switches. That is, if X denotes a switch or group of switches in either the 1 state or the open state, Theorem 1a defines the state of the total network as totally dependent on the state of the switch function X.

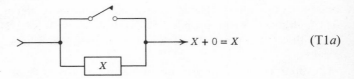

$$X + 0 = X \qquad\qquad\text{(T1}a)$$

That is, if X is closed, the network has the characteristics of a closed network. If X is open, the network has the characteristics of an open network. This is apparent when viewed as an open switch in parallel with the network X. In a dual manner, the " $\cdot$ " or AND function connotes a series connection of switches. Based upon this assumption, Theorem 1b is a series connection of the switch function X and a closed switch. Therefore the state of the total

$$X \cdot 1 = X \qquad\qquad\text{(T1}b)$$

network is again totally dependent on whether or not the switch function X is closed or open (1 or 0).

In the formal sense Theorems 1a and 1b are proved by a technique known as deductive analysis. That is, Postulates 2 and 3 are successively applied to account for all possible states of X, verifying that Theorems 1a and 1b are valid equalities.

Theorem 2a $X + 1 = 1.$

Theorem 2b $X \cdot 0 = 0.$

Theorem 3a $X + X = X.$

Theorem 3b $X \cdot X = X.$

Theorem 4a $\overline{(X)} = \overline{X}.$

Theorem 4b $\overline{(\overline{X})} = X.$

Theorem 5a $X + \overline{X} = 1.$

Theorem 5b $X \cdot \overline{X} = 0.$

The above theorems complete the formal arithmetic fundamentals of Boolean algebra; all further theorems are based on these simple principles. The above theorems can be proved by deductive analysis. The theorems can often be more readily remembered by means of a pictorial illustration.

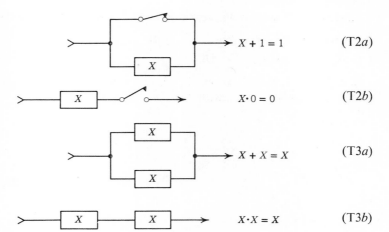

$$X + 1 = 1 \qquad (T2a)$$

$$X \cdot 0 = 0 \qquad (T2b)$$

$$X + X = X \qquad (T3a)$$

$$X \cdot X = X \qquad (T3b)$$

Theorem 4 illustrates the ordinary algebraic relationship of the parentheses. Theorems 5a and 5b complete the concept that $1 + 0 = 1$ (from Postulate 4b) and $1 \cdot 0 = 0$ (from Postulate 4a).

Some examples of the uses of these theorems follow.

Theorem 2a states that $X + 1 = 1$. As X is an unspecified or generic variable this theorem implies that any function OR'ed with 1 is 1. Thus

EXAMPLE 2.1. $A + B + C + 1 = 1$
       where $X = A + B + C.$

EXAMPLE 2.2. $A + BC(D + E) + 1 = 1$
       where $X = A + BC(D + E).$

In a like manner anything AND'ed with 0 is 0, from Theorem 2b. Thus

EXAMPLE 2.3. $(AB + C) \cdot 0 = 0$
       where $X = AB + C.$

EXAMPLE 2.4. $(A + B)(B + C) \cdot 0 = 0$
       where $X = (A + B)(B + C)$

Also, from Theorem 3a, anything AND'ed with itself is itself. Thus

EXAMPLE 2.5. $(A + BC)(A + BC) = A + BC.$

EXAMPLE 2.6. $(AB)(AB) = AB.$

EXAMPLE 2.7. $AA = A.$

Finally, from Theorem 3*b*, anything OR'ed with itself is also itself. Thus

EXAMPLE 2.8. $A + A + B + B = A + B$.

EXAMPLE 2.9. $AB + AB = AB$.

Some practical applications of these theorems will illustrate the techniques of applying them with the following examples:

Simplify:

EXAMPLE 2.10.

AAB

$AAB = AB$	since $AA = A$ from Theorem 3*b*.

EXAMPLE 2.11.

$(A\bar{B} + A\bar{B}) \cdot 1$

$(A\bar{B} + A\bar{B}) \cdot 1 = (A\bar{B}) \cdot 1$	from Theorem 3*a*.
$= A\bar{B}$	from Theorem 1*b*.

EXAMPLE 2.12.

$A\bar{A} + BC$

$A\bar{A} + BC = 0 + BC$	from Theorem 5*b*.
$= BC$	from Theorem 1*a*.

EXAMPLE 2.13.

$A + \bar{A} + BC + \bar{B}\bar{C}$

$A + \bar{A} + BC + \bar{B}\bar{C} = 1 + BC + \bar{B}\bar{C}$	from Theorem 5*a*.
$= 1$	from Theorem 2*a*.

EXAMPLE 2.14.

$(AB + C)C\bar{C}$

$(AB + C)C\bar{C} = (AB + C)0$	from Theorem 5*b*.
$= 0$	from Theorem 2*b*.

Theorem 6a	$X(X + Y) = X$.
Theorem 6b	$X + XY = X$.
Theorem 7a	$X(\bar{X} + Y) = XY$.
Theorem 7b	$X + \bar{X}Y = X + Y$.
Theorem 8a	$XY + XZ = X(Y + Z)$.
Theorem 8b	$(X + Y)(X + Z) = X + YZ$.
Theorem 9a	$XY + YZ + \bar{X}Z = XY + \bar{X}Z$.
Theorem 9b	$(X + Y)(\bar{X} + Z) = XZ + \bar{X}Y$.

The above theorems are extremely useful in algebraic manipulation of Boolean functions. As will be seen, the analysis and implementation of binary functions involves a certain degree of skill in recognizing theorems within equations and the manipulation of these equations by use of the theorems.

These theorems may be proved in a variety of ways, but the introduction of the Karnaugh map at this time seems appropriate because it is the most useful single tool developed for the analysis and manipulation of binary functions.

Each variable in Boolean algebra can have either of two states, 1 or 0. Thus two variables taken together can have 2^2 or four states. That is, the variable A can be present as A or as $\bar{A}$ (1 or 0). A second variable, B, can also be present as B or $\bar{B}$. These two variables taken together can be present as AB, $A\bar{B}$, $\bar{A}B$, or $\bar{A}\bar{B}$. If a state of 1 is assigned to the uncomplemented variable and 0 is assigned to the complemented variable the four states listed above can be written as 11, 10, 01, and 00. This is quite important. Three variables can be written in 2^3 different ways, and n variables can be written in 2^n different ways. This procedure gets quite complex as the number of variables increases.

An approach to a systematic listing of all the binary states that a group of variables can take is a table of combinations, or truth table. The truth table is nothing more than an orderly listing of the various combinations in a binary numbering sequence. That is, given three variables A, B, and C, we know there are 2^3 or eight different arrangements of these variables, taken three at a time. The truth table or table of combinations is a listing of the binary numbers in orderly sequence as shown in Table 2.1. A table of combinations is quite useful in analyzing certain functions, but it lacks compactness and utility.

TABLE 2.1   Table of Combinations

No.	A	B	C	Sequence
0	0	0	0	$\bar{A}\bar{B}\bar{C}$
1	0	0	1	$\bar{A}\bar{B}C$
2	0	1	0	$\bar{A}B\bar{C}$
3	0	1	1	$\bar{A}BC$
4	1	0	0	$A\bar{B}\bar{C}$
5	1	0	1	$A\bar{B}C$
6	1	1	0	$AB\bar{C}$
7	1	1	1	ABC

A more eloquent and useful presentation of the combinations is the Karnaugh map. This is a matrix array of all the possible combinations that a group of variables can take. For instance, a single variable can exist as A or $\bar{A}$, or as 1 or 0. Thus two squares can represent this variable.

A	$\bar{A}$
1	0

However, the existence of two squares is meaningless unless it is related to the calculus of propositions. Let it be said that a single square contains all the possible combinations of the function. Within this single square (Fig. 2.1) is a domain where the function is true and another domain where the function is false. In a like manner, a matrix to describe two variables

A TRUE 1	$\bar{A}$ FALSE 0

Figure 2.1

can be made of four different cells within the total box, each cell representing a unique combination of the two variables (see Fig. 2.2). It can be said that the function A is contained in the two cells that make up the right-hand

$\bar{A}\bar{B}$	$A\bar{B}$
$\bar{A}B$	AB

Figure 2.2

column whereas the variable $\bar{A}$ is contained in the two cells of the left-hand column, as illustrated in Figure 2.3.

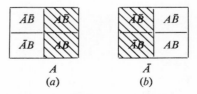

A	$\bar{A}$
(a)	(b)

Figure 2.3

If we assign $A = 1$, thus $\bar{A} = 0$; and $B = 1$, thus $\bar{B} = 0$, we can make assignments to the cells as shown in Figure 2.4. The two combinations of A

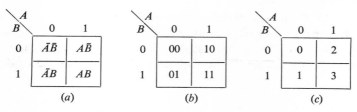

Figure 2.4 Maps of function AB

are listed across the top whereas the two combinations of B are listed down the side. The intersections of these combinations combine to form a unique combination of the two variables.

The first map (Fig. 2.4a) denotes the cells as functions of A and B. The second map (b) illustrates the binary state associated with each cell. Note the assignment of a 1 state to the uncomplemented variable and a 0 to the complemented variable. The third map (c) introduces the concept of a decimal number associated with a particular cell. The number in the cell is the decimal equivalent for the binary number of the cell. Thus

$$A\bar{B} = 10_{(2)} = 2_{(10)}.$$

This decimal equivalent of a binary state will be expanded upon and receive greater usage later.

Now consider Theorem 6b, $X + XY = X$. This is a two-variable problem and can be contained in a four-cell map, as shown in Figure 2.5. The variable X is contained in the two cells of the right-hand column. The function $X \cdot Y$ is contained in the single cell at the intersection of the right-hand

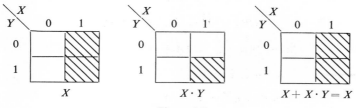

Figure 2.5

column, where $X = 1$, and the bottom row, where $Y = 1$. It can be seen that the function X contains or includes the function $X \cdot Y$ and therefore the function $X \cdot Y$ is redundant.

Theorem 7a, $X(\bar{X} + Y) = XY$, can be illustrated with a Karnaugh map as shown in Figure 2.6 by mapping the term X and the function $\bar{X} + Y$ separately. The term X occupies the right-hand column of the map, whereas the term $\bar{X} + Y$ fills the left-hand column related to $\bar{X}$ as well as the lower row related to Y. Because the term X is AND'ed with the function $\overline{X} + Y$, this implies the total area where both X and $\overline{X} + Y$ are true at the same time. This only occurs at the cell represented by the term $X \cdot Y$, as the theorem demands. Further proofs of the theorems will be left to the student.

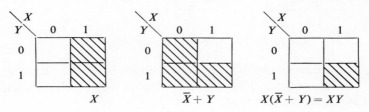

The following theorems are presented without proof, because the student is assumed to be somewhat familiar with the material or can review some of the references on the subject.

Theorem 10a $\overline{X + Y + Z + \cdots} = \overline{X} \cdot \overline{Y} \cdot \overline{Z} \cdots$.

Theorem 10b $\overline{X \cdot Y \cdot Z} = \overline{X} + \overline{Y} + \overline{Z} + \cdots$.

This is known as De Morgan's theorem, whereby the complement of a function is obtained by changing all " $\cdot$ " to " $+$ " and all " $+$ " to " $\cdot$ ", complementing all uncomplemented terms, and uncomplementing all complemented terms.

For example, the following functions are complemented thus:

EXAMPLE 2.15. $\overline{A + B \cdot C} = \overline{A} \cdot \overline{B} + \overline{C}$.

EXAMPLE 2.16. $\overline{A(BC + \overline{D})} = A + (\overline{B} + \overline{C})D$.

EXAMPLE 2.17. $\overline{A\overline{B}C + D(\overline{A} + B)} = (\overline{A} + B + \overline{C})(\overline{D} + A\overline{B})$.

Theorem 11a $XY + \overline{X}Y = Y$.

Theorem 11b $(X + Y)(\overline{X} + Y) = Y$.

Summary of Theorems

Theorem   1a $X + 0 = X$.

Theorem   1b $X \cdot 1 = X$.

Theorem   2a $X + 1 = 1$.

Theorem   2b $X \cdot 0 = 0$.

Theorem *3a* $X + X = X.$

Theorem *3b* $X \cdot X = X.$

Theorem *4a* $(\overline{X}) = \overline{X}.$

Theorem *4b* $(\overline{\overline{X}}) = X.$

Theorem *5a* $X + \overline{X} = 1.$

Theorem *5b* $X \cdot \overline{X} = 0.$

Theorem *6a* $X(X + Y) = X.$

Theorem *6b* $X + XY = X.$

Theorem *7a* $X(\overline{X} + Y) = XY.$

Theorem *7b* $X + \overline{X}Y = X + Y.$

Theorem *8a* $XY + XZ = X(Y + Z).$

Theorem *8b* $(X + Y)(X + Z) = X + YZ.$

Theorem *9a* $XY + YZ + \overline{X}Z = XY + \overline{X}Z.$

Theorem *9b* $(X + Y)(\overline{X} + Z) = XZ + \overline{X}Y.$

Theorem *10a* $\overline{X + Y + Z + \cdots} = \overline{X} \cdot \overline{Y} \cdot \overline{Z} \cdots.$

Theorem *10b* $\overline{X \cdot Y \cdot Z \cdots} = \overline{X} + \overline{Y} + \overline{Z} + \cdots.$

Theorem *11a* $XY + \overline{X}Y = Y.$

Theorem *11b* $(X + Y)(\overline{X} + Y) = Y.$

2.4 STANDARD FORMS

There is a lot of reference made in texts to the standard sum form or the standard product form of an expression. These statements refer to the two basic elementary forms in which a Boolean algebraic expression can be written. That is, the expression $AB + \overline{B}C$ is an OR'ing of the two AND'ed terms. The AND'ed terms, AB and $\overline{B}C$, are called product terms. The OR'ing of things is called a sum of things. Thus the above expression is a sum of products. This sum of products is called a standard sum form.

For example, $AB + C(\overline{A} + BD)$ is a hybrid function and only after expanding or multiplying through by C can it become a sum of products, $AB + \overline{A}C + BCD$.

In a like manner the standard product form is a product of sums.

That is, the expression $(A + B)(C + D)$ is a product of two sum terms. The function $A\bar{B} + \bar{A}B$ can also be written as $(A + B)(\bar{A} + \bar{B})$. Similarly, the function $\bar{A}\bar{B}\bar{C} + BC$ can be written as $(B + \bar{C})(\bar{A} + B)(\bar{B} + C)$. The ability to manipulate algebraic expressions is a must in digital implementations. Quite often it is desirable to be able to write a product of sums form or a sum of products form in order to achieve optimum network design. Algebraic manipulation need not always depend entirely on one's ability to remember the theorems or recognize them, but rather on one's ability to reduce the expression to a standard form, map it via the Karnaugh map, and then perform the game of examining the various forms to which the expression may be reduced. This ability to change, rearrange, reduce, and expand rapidly is an art. The skilled logic designer can rewrite equations as a skilled musician plays a tune. As with musical art, experience and practice are required.

2.5 ALGEBRAIC MANIPULATION

It is often true that the simplest algebraic expression is not the cheapest or best form to implement in real hardware. Redundant terms can be quite useful in complex problems to reduce the actual logic gate count. For example, given the functions

$$f = \bar{A}\bar{C} + \bar{B}\bar{C} \quad \text{and} \quad g = B\bar{C} + A\bar{C},$$

it can be shown that these expressions may be implemented more cheaply if they are written as

$$f = \bar{A}\bar{C} + A\bar{B}\bar{C} \quad \text{and} \quad g = B\bar{C} + A\bar{B}\bar{C}.$$

The two functions have the term $A\bar{B}\bar{C}$ in common, and this can be shared in the implementation process. It can be shown, therefore, that the introduction of the redundant A variable in the f function and the $\bar{B}$ variable in the g function actually reduces cost.

The concern at this point, however, is to illustrate how the theorems are useful in manipulation and minimization of algebraic expressions. That is, how does one go about changing the form of f from the first expression to the second, or vice versa? This is where experience in Boolean algebra is useful. A few examples will be used to illustrate.

EXAMPLE 2.18 $\quad f = \bar{A}\bar{C} + \bar{B}\bar{C}$
$\qquad\qquad\quad = \bar{C}(\bar{A} + \bar{B})$
$\qquad\qquad\quad = \bar{C}(\bar{A} + A\bar{B})$ $\qquad\qquad\qquad$ (T7b)
$\qquad\qquad\quad = \bar{A}\bar{C} + A\bar{B}\bar{C}.$

EXAMPLE 2.19 $\quad g = B\bar{C} + A\bar{B}\bar{C}$
$$= \bar{C}(B + A\bar{B}) \qquad\qquad (T7b)$$
$$= \bar{C}(B + A)$$
$$= B\bar{C} + A\bar{C}.$$

The first example illustrates how expansion of a function into a canonical standard sum form can be useful. Expansion and regrouping are used to accomplish the objective. The second example shows how expansion results in eventual simplification. Both these examples are forced; that is, the desired result is known and it is required to verify the answer. Some examples that may not be so obvious follow.

EXAMPLE 2.20 $\quad f = A\bar{B}C + \bar{A}\bar{B}C$
$$= \bar{B}C(A + \bar{A})$$
$$= \bar{B}C. \qquad\qquad (T5a)$$

EXAMPLE 2.21 $\quad f = AC + BC + \bar{A}B$
$$= AC + BC(A + \bar{A}) + \bar{A}B \qquad\qquad (T5a)$$
$$= AC + \underbrace{ABC + \bar{A}BC} + \underbrace{\bar{A}B}$$

$$= AC(1 + B) + \bar{A}B(C + 1) \qquad\qquad (T2a)$$
$$= AC(1) + \bar{A}B(1) \qquad\qquad (T1b)$$
$$= AC + \bar{A}B.$$

EXAMPLE 2.22 $\quad f = \bar{A} + B + \bar{C} + A\bar{B}C \qquad\qquad (T10a)$
$$= \overline{(A\bar{B}C)} + A\bar{B}C \qquad\qquad (T5a)$$
$$= 1.$$

EXAMPLE 2.23 $\quad f = (A + BC)(A + CD) \qquad\qquad (T8b)$
$$= A + BCD.$$

EXAMPLE 2.24 $\quad f = AB + C(AB + \bar{C})$
$$= AB + ABC + C\bar{C} \qquad\qquad (T5b)$$
$$= AB + ABC + 0 \qquad\qquad (T1a)$$
$$= AB + ABC$$
$$= AB(1 + C) \qquad\qquad (T2a)$$
$$= AB.$$

PROBLEMS

1. Simplify:
   (a) $A\bar{B} + \bar{A}\bar{B}C$.
   (b) $AB + AB\bar{C}D + ABC\bar{D}$.
   (c) $\bar{A}BC + A(\bar{A}C + B\bar{C})$.

    (d) $\bar{D}(B + \bar{C}D) + \bar{B}\bar{D}$.

    (e) $\bar{A}B\bar{C}D + AB\bar{C}D$.

    (f) $(A + \bar{C}D)(\bar{A} + \bar{C}D)$.

    (g) $BCD + B\bar{C}D$.

    (h) $(A + \bar{B})(A + B)$.

    (i) $B(C + \bar{A}D) + \bar{B}(C + \bar{A}D)$.

    (j) $(A + B + \bar{C})(\bar{A} + B + \bar{C})$.

    (k) $(\bar{A} + \bar{B} + \bar{C} + D)(\bar{A} + B + \bar{C})$.

    (l) $\bar{A}\bar{B}C\bar{D} + \bar{A}\bar{B}CD + A\bar{B}C\bar{D} + A\bar{B}CD$.

    (m) $BC\bar{D} + ABC\bar{D} + \bar{A}BC\bar{D}$.

    (n) $E(A\bar{B} + C\bar{E}) + \bar{E}(\bar{A}B + \bar{C}E)$.

    (o) $ABC + (\bar{A} + \bar{B} + \bar{C})$.

    (p) $EF\bar{G} + A\bar{B}\bar{G} + \bar{C}EF\bar{G} + \bar{E}\bar{F}\bar{G} + \bar{G}$.

    (q) $B\bar{D}E + \bar{A}C\bar{E} + \bar{B}D(A\bar{D} + \bar{B}\bar{D}E) + \bar{D}E$.

2. Prove the following equalities:

    (a) $A + B + C = (A + B)(\bar{A} + B) + (C + \bar{D})(C + D) + (A + E)(A + \bar{E})$.

    (b) $B + D = ABC + \bar{A}BC + B\bar{C} + AD + \bar{A}D$.

    (c) $B\bar{C} + BD = (A + B)(\bar{C} + D)(\bar{A} + B)$.

    (d) $AB(C + D) = (C + D)(\bar{A} + B)(A + \bar{B})(A + B)$.

    (e) $ADE + (\bar{A} + \bar{D})G = (AD + G)(\bar{A} + \bar{D} + E)$.

    (f) $AC(B + \bar{D}) + AC(\bar{B} + E) = AC$.

3. Simplify:

    (a) $A\bar{B} + \bar{A}\bar{B}C + \bar{A}\bar{B}C$.

    (b) $\bar{A}\bar{B} + \bar{A}B\bar{C} + \bar{A}C$.

    (c) $AD + BCD + \bar{A}BC$.

    (d) $BD + (\bar{B} + \bar{D})C$.

    (e) $CEF + BC(D + E) + \bar{A}B(A + \bar{B}) + \bar{C}EF$.

    (f) $(A + \bar{B} + D)(\bar{A} + \bar{B} + D) + B\bar{D} + A\bar{C}D + \bar{A}B\bar{C}D$.

    (g) $AC + \bar{A}DE + B\bar{D}F + CDE + \bar{A}BEF$.

    (h) $(A + \bar{B} + D)(\bar{A} + B + D)(A + B + D)$.

    (i) $(A + B)\bar{C} + \bar{A}\bar{B} + C$.

    (j) $AB(\bar{C} + DE) + C(AB + \bar{C}E)$.

    (k) $(AB + \bar{C})D + (\bar{A} + \bar{B})C$.

    (l) $BC\bar{D} + \bar{B}EF + \bar{C}EF + DEF$.

    (m) $\bar{A}C + B\bar{C} + A\bar{B}D + A\bar{C}D + \bar{A}B$.

4. Prove equality:

    (a) $AC + \bar{A}\bar{D} = (\bar{A} + C)(A + \bar{D})$.

    (b) $\bar{B}C + \bar{A}CD = \bar{B}CD + \bar{B}C\bar{D} + \bar{A}CD$.

    (c) $A\bar{B} + \bar{A}B = \overline{AB + \bar{A}\bar{B}}$.

    (d) $B\bar{C}D + \bar{A}\bar{B}\bar{C} + AB\bar{D} + \bar{A}\bar{C} = (B + \bar{C})(A + \bar{C})(\bar{A} + \bar{C} + \bar{D})(\bar{A} + B)$.

(e) $A\bar{C}E + \bar{B}D\bar{E} = A\bar{B}\bar{C}D + A\bar{C}DE + \bar{B}D\bar{E} + A\bar{C}\bar{D}E.$
(f) $(A + BC)(\bar{A} + \bar{B} + \bar{C}) = \bar{A}BC + A\bar{B} + A\bar{C}.$
(g) $A\bar{B}C + AB\bar{C} = C[A\bar{B} + (\bar{B} + D)\bar{C}] + B(AB\bar{C}D + A\bar{C}\bar{D}).$
(h) $\bar{B}\bar{C}\bar{D} + AC\bar{D} + BCD + \bar{A}\bar{C}D = \bar{A}B\bar{C} + A\bar{B}\bar{D} + ABC + \bar{A}BD.$
(i) $\bar{A}\bar{C}\bar{D} + \bar{A}C\bar{D} = \bar{A}\bar{B}\bar{D} + \bar{A}B\bar{D}.$
(j) $\bar{A}\bar{B}\bar{D} + A\bar{B}C + \bar{B}\bar{C}D = \overline{\bar{B}(\bar{A} + C + D)(A + \bar{C} + \bar{D})}.$
(k) $A\bar{B}\bar{D} + BC + CD = \overline{\bar{A}\bar{B}\bar{D} + B\bar{C} + \bar{C}D}.$

5. Complement:

(a) $A\bar{B} + BC\bar{D}.$
(b) $B[\bar{A}C + D(C + \bar{E})].$
(c) $(\bar{A} + B + C)(A + \bar{B}C).$
(d) $(BC + \bar{E})A\bar{B} + CE + BD(\bar{A}B + D).$
(e) $(\bar{A}B + CD)(\bar{B}D + E + FG).$
(f) $A(B + C)(\bar{A} + D)(\bar{C}D + B).$
(g) $A\bar{B}C + \bar{A}B\bar{C} + ABC.$
(h) $AE + \bar{A}B(C + D) + EF(A\bar{B} + C\bar{D}).$
(i) $\bar{A}B + \bar{B}CD + A(CD + \bar{E}).$
(j) $(\bar{A} + B)(A + \bar{B} + C)(\bar{B} + C + DEF).$

3

MINIMIZATION AIDS

3.1 INTRODUCTION

Minimization involves reducing a Boolean algebraic expression to some minimal form. Any minimization tool in Boolean is based on the algebraic theorems. Algebraic reduction of Boolean functions is not easy and requires considerable experience, judgment, and luck. This becomes more apparent as the complexity of the function increases. As a result extensive effort has been devoted toward developing techniques, aids, tools, or gimmicks that will allow the logic designer to minimize a function. The Venn diagram, Veitch diagram, Karnaugh map, Quine-McCluskey method, and other techniques have all been developed with but one objective—to allow the designer to arrive at a minimal expression as rapidly as possible with the least amount of effort.

3.2 ALGEBRA

Algebraic theorems provide the fundamental tools of minimization. Such an expression as $A\bar{B} + \bar{A}\bar{B}$ is obviously dependent only on $\bar{B}$. But it is not so obvious that the expression $A\bar{B} + \bar{B}C + \bar{A}C$ can be exactly represented by $A\bar{B} + \bar{A}C$. The theorems help in recognizing these identities and provide the basis for these reductions, but they are clumsy to apply.

3.3 VENN DIAGRAMS

The Venn diagram utilizes adjacent and overlapping circles to define geographical areas representing the different combinations of variables. This is

32

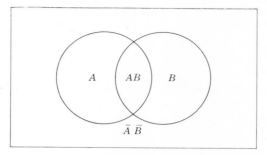

Figure 3.1 Venn diagram.

shown in Figure 3.1. The rectangle defines the universe; that is, it surrounds the area and establishes boundaries. Inside this area is a circle defining the domain of A. It can be said that A is true inside the circle and is not true outside the circle. The second overlapping circle defines the domain of B. It can be said that B is true inside this circle and is not true outside its boundaries. Thus the domain outside both circles, is, by definition, $\bar{A}$ and $\bar{B}$. The domain within the area contained by both circles must be A AND B. The four combinational states of two variables can be thus represented. However, it is apparent that this technique rapidly reaches a practical limit with three variables.

3.4 TABLE OF COMBINATIONS

The truth table or table of combinations may have been the next attempt at developing a minimization tool. Figure 3.2 is a table of combinations for three variables. There are eight possible combinations of three binary variables, and these have been listed in numerical order. The designation of a complemented variable by 0 and an uncomplemented variable by 1 is apparent.

No.	A	B	C	Function
0	0	0	0	$\bar{A}\bar{B}\bar{C}$
1	0	0	1	$\bar{A}\bar{B}C$
2	0	1	0	$\bar{A}B\bar{C}$
3	0	1	1	$\bar{A}BC$
4	1	0	0	$A\bar{B}\bar{C}$
5	1	0	1	$A\bar{B}C$
6	1	1	0	$AB\bar{C}$
7	1	1	1	ABC

Figure 3.2 Table of combinations.

A comparison of row 4 with row 5 shows that the variable C is a redundant variable when these two rows appear in a single function. That is, row 4 and row 5 would be written in a sum form as $A\bar{B}\bar{C} + A\bar{B}C$. Application of the theorem $XY + \bar{X}Y = Y$ provides the aid for reducing the sum of these two terms to the single term $A\bar{B}$. This implies that C is a redundant variable; that is, it is not needed for the solution of the sum of numerical 4 and 5. This is apparent from the truth table, where C assumes the state of 1 and 0 while A and B remain constant. In other words, if there is only a one-variable change between the sum of two terms this single variable is redundant and can be eliminated.

The sum of row 3 and row 7 is independent of the variable A. This is evident because A is the only variable that changes and a function containing these two rows is $\bar{A}BC + ABC = BC(A + \bar{A}) = BC$.

As an example of the use of the table of combinations, minimize the earlier example of $A\bar{B} + \bar{B}C + \bar{A}C$. The first step is to list the combinations of the three variables as shown in Figure 3.3. All possible combinations of the three variables must be accounted for. Thus $f = A\bar{B} + \bar{B}C + \bar{A}C$ is 1 if $A\bar{B}$ alone is 1. Therefore wherever $A\bar{B}$ occurs in the table the function is 1. This is equivalent to expanding the term $A\bar{B}$ into its canonical form of $A\bar{B}(C + \bar{C}) = A\bar{B}C + A\bar{B}\bar{C}$ and is represented by rows 4 and 5. The second term, $\bar{B}C$, produces a 1 output for rows 1 and 5, whereas the third term, $\bar{A}C$, requires an entry for rows 1 and 3. It is evident from the truth table in Figure 3.3. that the term $\bar{A}C$ accounts for one of the $\bar{B}C$ terms whereas $A\bar{B}$ contains the second $\bar{B}C$ term. Therefore $\bar{B}C$ is a redundant term and is not necessary as a solution.

The truth table is a convenient tool for analysis and definition. It is useful to illustrate the various combinations that a function represents: this is analysis. The function $f = A\bar{B} + \bar{B}C + \bar{A}C$ may also be written as $f = \Sigma\,(1,3,4,5)$. This numerical classification is complete in that it does not depend on the alphabet and gives all the canonical terms. By convention an

No.	A	B	C	$f = A\bar{B} +$	$\bar{B}C +$	$\bar{A}C$
0	0	0	0	0		
1	0	0	1	1	$\bar{B}C$	$\bar{A}C$
2	0	1	0	0		
3	0	1	1	1		$\bar{A}C$
4	1	0	0	1	$A\bar{B}$	
5	1	0	1	1	$A\bar{B}$	$\bar{B}C$
6	1	1	0	0		
7	1	1	1	0		

Figure 3.3.

No.	A	B	C	D	f	
0	0	0	0	0	0	
1	0	0	0	1	0	
2	0	0	1	0	0	
3	0	0	1	1	0	
4	0	1	0	0	0	
5	0	1	0	1	1	$\bar{A}B\bar{C}D$
6	0	1	1	0	0	
7	0	1	1	1	1	$\bar{A}BCD$
8	1	0	0	0	0	
9	1	0	0	1	0	
10	1	0	1	0	0	
11	1	0	1	1	0	
12	1	1	0	0	0	
13	1	1	0	1	1	$AB\bar{C}D$
14	1	1	1	0	0	
15	1	1	1	1	1	$ABCD$

Braces: rows 5,7 grouped as $\bar{A}BD$; rows 13,15 grouped as ABD; overall group BD.

$$f = \Sigma\,(5,7,13,15)$$
$$= \bar{A}B\bar{C}D + \bar{A}BCD + AB\bar{C}D + ABCD$$
$$= \bar{A}BD + ABD$$
$$= BD.$$

Figure 3.4.

expression written in this manner implies that these are the numerical terms for which the function is to be true, and that for all other combinations the function is false. Referring to Figure 3.4, the Σ sign, signifies those combinations for which a standard sum of products form would be written.

The truth table is also convenient for synthesis. This is the conversion of a requirement into an algebraic expression. Or it may be said that synthesis is just the characterization of a function in a table of combinations. Because the synthesis or analysis of a function essentially defines an output or state for each and every combination of the variables, a table of combinations is useful inasmuch as it lists all the possible combinations in a systematic manner.

For example, synthesize a function that will provide a 1 output for the numerical states 5, 7, 13, and 15. Because the numerical state 15 is required, there must be at least four variables to have this many states. More than four variables could be used, but they would be of no value. A table of combinations for four variables is shown in Figure 3.4. The problem is for $f = \Sigma\,(5,7,13,15)$. An inspection of the table shows these states to be $\bar{A}B\bar{C}D$, $\bar{A}BCD$, $AB\bar{C}D$, and $ABCD$. The sum of these four terms forms a canonical expression of the required function. An inspection of the $\bar{A}B\bar{C}D$

and $\overline{A}BCD$ terms indicates that C is redundant and can be eliminated. The terms $AB\overline{C}D$ and $ABCD$ contain the redundant term C also. This is apparent in the figure, where C is the only variable that changes between states 5 and 7 as well as 13 and 15. Thus C is a redundant variable.

This produces the two terms $\overline{A}BD$ and ABD, which can also be written as 011 and 111. Again the one-variable change is evident, and so the theorem $XY + \overline{X}Y = Y$ can be applied to eliminate the variable A. Thus the two-variable term BD alone is sufficient to define all four states required of the function. Another way of saying this is that the term BD (in a four-variable function) contains all the combinations of A and C required in this example, and therefore it is not necessary to use them explicitly.

Minimization by use of the truth table is not immediately evident, and experience is required to develop any significant skill in its use. It is used quite often for synthesis and analysis, however, because it makes sense to those not familiar with more advanced aids. Thus the logic designer will use it to explain a condition to a systems designer or a circuit designer.

3.5 VEITCH DIAGRAMS

The Veitch diagram, developed by E. W. Veitch in 1952, is a refinement of the Venn diagram in that circles are replaced by squares and arranged in the form of a matrix. Figure 3.5 illustrates a Veitch diagram for two and three variables.

The idea behind diagrams of this type is to present graphically the various combinations in such a manner that minimization is obvious, or at least simplified. An inspection of the various cells in the matrices of Figure 3.5 reveals that there is only a one-variable change between any two adjacent cells. Each cell is identified by a singular combination of the variables. The variable A, in the three-variable map, is defined as an uncomplemented variable for the two adjacent left-hand columns. It is therefore understood that $\overline{A}$ defines the two adjacent right-hand columns. The variable B is contained in the four cells across the top whereas $\overline{B}$ is contained in the four cells along the bottom. The variable C is contained in the two inside columns

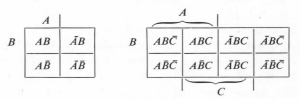

Figure 3.5 Veitch diagrams.

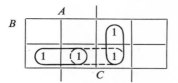

Figure 3.6 Mapping $f = A\bar{B} + \bar{B}C + \bar{A}C$.

whereas $\bar{C}$ is defined as being contained in the two outside columns. As a result of this assignment of the variables, any given one of the eight cells defines one of the eight combinational state of the three variables.

An application of this technique can be illustrated by using the previous example of $f = A\bar{B} + \bar{B}C + \bar{A}C$. This function would be "mapped" in the Veitch diagram by inserting a 1 in each cell for which the function is 1. Figure 3.6 contains a 1 in the cells defining the states $\bar{A}\bar{B}C$, $\bar{A}BC$, $A\bar{B}\bar{C}$, and $A\bar{B}C$. This is similar to the truth table in Figure 3.3, wherein the state of the function must be identified for all possible combination of the variables. If a 1 is not present in a given cell, a 0 state is present. This must be true because the function, by definition, can only be a logical 1 or a logical 0.

Inspection of the two adjacent cells $A\bar{B}\bar{C}$ and $A\bar{B}C$ indicates that whereas A and B remain constant, C is the single variable that changes. Therefore C is a redundant variable. Inspection of the two cells containing $\bar{A}\bar{B}C$ and $\bar{A}BC$ clearly shows that B is the only variable that changes, and thus it is the redundant variable. Furthermore, the summing of the two terms $A\bar{B}$ and $\bar{A}C$ clearly contains all the 1 states of the function and totally defines the function. The grouping of adjacent cells is in conformity with the theorem $XY + \bar{X}Y = Y$. The term $\bar{B}C$ in the original function comes from the two adjacent cells $A\bar{B}C$ and $\bar{A}\bar{B}C$. These two terms are shown dotted in Figure 3.6 and produce the single redundant term $\bar{B}C$. It is redundant because the term $A\bar{B}C$ is contained in the $A\bar{B}$ term and the $\bar{A}\bar{B}C$ term is contained in $\bar{A}C$.

The power of the Veitch diagram is that it provides a pictorial means for analysis and minimization. Minimization can now be accomplished by inspection of a diagram rather than tedious application of algebraic theorems.

3.6 KARNAUGH MAPS

New ideas did not stop with the introduction of the Veitch diagram. An improvement was made by G. Karnaugh in 1953, who rearranged the alphabetical assignments and substituted 1 and 0 for the letters as shown in Figure 3.7. Although many logic designers still use the Veitch assignments,

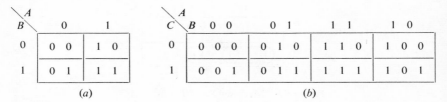

Figure 3.7   Karnaugh maps: (*a*) two-variable map; (*b*) three-variable map.

the assignments by Karnaugh are usually easier to comprehend and utilize. Therefore the Karnaugh map will be the main tool used in this book.

The Karnaugh map is an orderly arrangement of squares with assignments such that the difference between any two adjacent squares is a one-variable change. The map must contain a square or cell for each unique combination of variables. A map for two variables must contain four cells, because there are 2^2 different combinations of two variables. A map for three variables must contain 2^3 or eight cells, and a map of n variables must contain 2^n cells. An assignment of 1 for an uncomplemented variable and 0 for a complemented variable is made such that the term $A\bar{B}C$ is equivalent to the binary notation 101. This assignment also leads to the decimal numerical designation of these combinations in the same manner as in the table of combinations. Thus $A\bar{B}C = 101 = 5$ for a three-variable function. Figure 3.8 shows the three ways to define each cell of a three-variable function. This is consistent with the table of combinations in Figure 3.2.

The alphabetical variables are identified at the upper left-hand corner of the box. The diagonal line indicates that the variables A and B are represented by the binary notations across the top of the matrix and are contained in the vertical column below each assignment. The variable C is assigned down the side of the matrix and is represented by horizontal rows

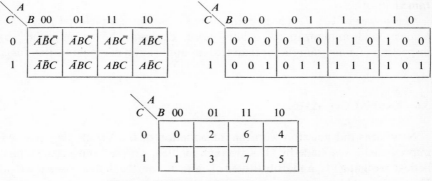

Figure 3.8   Three-variable Karnaugh map.

C \ A
D \ B

D \ B	00	01	11	10
00	0	4	12	8
01	1	5	13	9
11	3	7	15	11
10	2	6	14	10

(a)

C \ A
D \ B

D \ B E	00	01	11	10
000	0	8	24	16
001	1	9	25	17
011	3	11	27	19
010	2	10	26	18
110	6	14	30	22
111	7	15	31	23
101	5	13	29	21
100	4	12	28	20

(b)

C \ A
D \ B

D \ B	00	01	11	10
0 00				
0 01				
0 11				
E 0 10				
1 00				
1 01				
1 11				
1 10				

(c)

Figure 3.9.

within the matrix. Each cell represents a unique combination of the variables. Figure 3.9*a* and *b* illustrate the arrangement of a Karnaugh map for four and five variables with appropriate decimal designations within the cells. Figure 3.9*c* illustrates another way to represent a five-variable map by the use of two four-variable maps. Any arrangement is valid and depends largely on the preference of the user.

There are times when it is convenient to maintain a consistent assignment of decimal weight to the variables; that is, adopt a convention whereby the letter A always represents 2^0 or the least significant bit. Then B represents 2^1, C represents 2^2, and so on for as many variables as required. This convention is useful when dealing with numerical problems. An assignment of variables under this convention is shown in Figure 3.10 for three, four, and

B over A, C at left (a) three-variable map:

C \ A	00	01	11	10
0	0	1	3	2
1	4	5	7	6

(a)

D\B, C\A (b) four-variable map:

C \ A	00	01	11	10
00	0	1	3	2
01	4	5	7	6
11	12	13	15	14
10	8	9	11	10

(b)

E\B, D\A, C (c) five-variable map:

D \ A	00	01	11	10
000	0	1	3	2
001	4	5	7	6
011	12	13	15	14
010	8	9	11	10
110	24	25	27	26
111	28	29	31	30
101	20	21	23	22
100	16	17	19	18

(c)

Figure 3.10 Karnaugh maps: (a) three-variable map; (b) four-variable map; (c) five-variable map.

five variables. The uniqueness of this assignment lies in the consistent location of numerical values for the cells. Decimal 6 always appears in the second cell down in the fourth column, whereas 8 is always located in the fourth row of the first column. Furthermore, if A is always the least significant bit, the use of E identifies the set as at least a 5-bit word or a five-variable problem.

The Karnaugh map technique is thought to be the most valuable tool available for dealing with Boolean functions. It provides instant recognition of basic patterns, can be used to obtain all possible combinations and minimal terms, and is easily applied to all varieties of complex problems.

Minimization with the map is accomplished through recognition of basic patterns. The appearance of 1's in adjacent cells immediately identifies the presence of a redundant variable. Figure 3.11 illustrates some examples of minimizing with a three-variable map. Notice that the grouping of two cells eliminates one variable. Furthermore, the map is arranged in such a way that the ends can be considered reflective; that is, adjacent.

Figures 3.12 and 3.13 illustrate the grouping of one, two, and four cells in a four-variable map. It takes all four variables to define a single cell of a four-variable map: the grouping of two cells eliminates one variable, the grouping of four cells eliminates two variables, and the grouping of eight cells eliminates three variables.

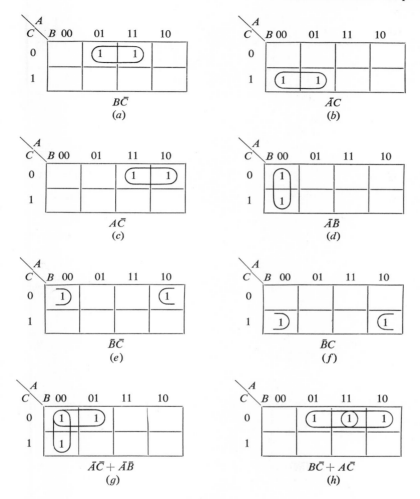

Figure 3.11.

Any given grouping of 1's in the Karnaugh map is identified by a product form. That is, the single cell in Figure 3.12a is defined as $\bar{A}B\bar{C}\bar{D}$. The grouping of two cells, as in Figure 3.12h, is identified by BCD. The grouping of four cells is identified by the product or AND'ing of two variables, as in Figure 3.13. Minimization involves the gathering of the various groups in the most efficient manner.

For example, the map shown in Figure 3.14 contains eight cells with 1's. In the numerical sense this represents the function defined by $\Sigma(2,3,4,7,$

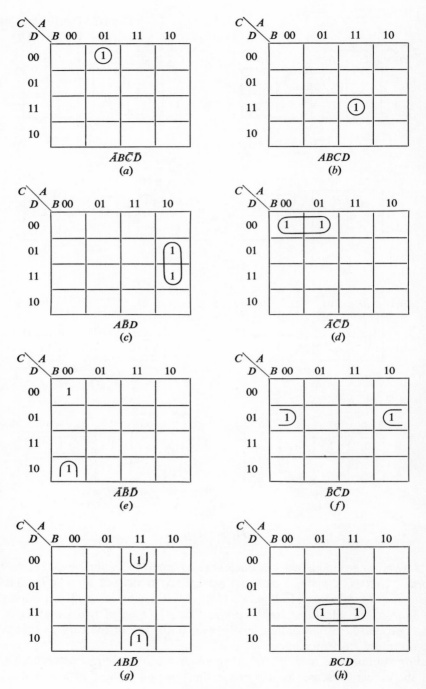

Figure 3.12.

42

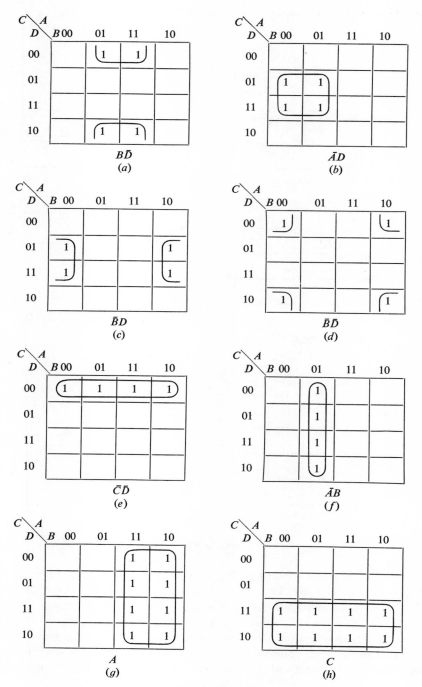

Figure 3.13.

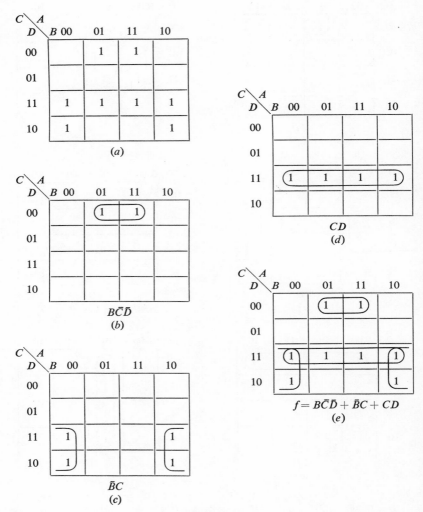

Figure 3.14.

10, 11, 12, 15) when referred to Figure 3.9a. By inspection of Figure 3.14a a grouping of the two 1's in cells 4 and 12 is described by the function $B\bar{C}\bar{D}$, as shown in Figure 3.14b. The four 1's in Figure 3.14c can be contained in the term $\bar{B}C$ while Figure 3.14d shows a grouping of four 1's described by the term CD. This accounts for all the 1's. A summation of these terms will then completely describe the required function with the least number of literals and with a minimal expression, as shown in Figure 3.14e.

This summing of terms is based on the theorem $X + 1 = 1$. That is, anything OR'ed with 1 is 1. Thus a function composed of a sum of terms is 1 if any single sum term is 1. The mapping of a sum of product terms is accomplished by inserting a 1 in each cell of a map containing a particular product term.

For example, given

$$f = A\bar{B}\bar{C} + AB\bar{C} + \bar{A}B\bar{C}.$$

This function is 1 if $A\bar{B}\bar{C}$ is 1. Therefore in a three-variable map a 1 is inserted in the cell representing the combination $A\bar{B}\bar{C}$. The function is also 1 if $AB\bar{C}$ is 1. Therefore, as shown in Figure 3.15, a 1 is inserted in the cell representative of $AB\bar{C}$. Finally, the function is 1 if $\bar{A}B\bar{C}$ is 1; therefore a 1 is inserted in this cell. There are no other possible combinations that will cause the function to be 1. Then, for any combination of the variables A, B, and C other than the three combinations specified, the function is 0. Once the map is complete, minimization can take place by proper grouping of the 1's. The function is 1 whenever $B\bar{C}$ is 1. The function is also 1 whenever $A\bar{C}$ is 1. Thus the summing of these terms will also totally define the function in a minimal expression. Inspection of the map of Figure 3.15 makes it quite clear that these are the only two terms required and that this is the only minimal expression for this function. The advantage of the map is that it gives a clear and complete picture of the function. It can immediately be determined if the reduction is unique or if there exist other minimal expressions just as valid. In addition it gives an insight into other forms or ways in which the expression can be manipulated. In actual implementation it is not always the minimal form that is used, but quite often one that depends on other related expressions.

For example, the previous function, $f = A\bar{C} + B\bar{C}$, can also be written as $f = \bar{C}(A + B)$. This expression can be obtained by mapping the 0's instead of the 1's. That is, the function f is 0 if $\bar{C}$ is 0. This is from the theorem $0 \cdot X = 0$. But for $\bar{C}$ to be 0 C must be 1. Therefore in the map of Figure 3.16 a 0 is inserted in the cells for $C = 1$. Also the function f is 0 whenever

$$f = A\bar{B}\bar{C} + AB\bar{C} + \bar{A}B\bar{C}$$
$$= B\bar{C} + A\bar{C}$$

Figure 3.15.

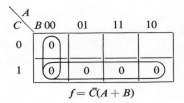

$$f = \bar{C}(A + B)$$

Figure 3.16.

the term $(A + B)$ is 0. In order for the term $(A + B)$ to be 0, both A and B must be 0. Therefore, in the cells for $\bar{A} \cdot \bar{B}$, place a 0.

The mapping of 0's and minimizing using the zeros is mostly a matter of experience. It may be easier to consider that, instead of mapping $f = \bar{C}(A + B)$, the actual mapping is of the function $\bar{f}$, because 0's are being mapped. Because, $\bar{f} = C + \bar{A}\bar{B}$ and is a sum of products, these terms are easy enough to find. Remember that the mapping is $\bar{f}$ and therefore entries in the map for the cells encompassing C are for $\bar{f}$ and are therefore 0's. This is also true for $\bar{A} \cdot \bar{B}$.

Some more examples of using the map method will provide a better insight into the value of this technique.

EXAMPLE 3.1. *Minimize $f = A\bar{B} + AB\bar{D} + AB\bar{C}D$.*

By algebraic means

$$
\begin{aligned}
f &= A\bar{B} + AB(\bar{D} + \bar{C}D), \\
&= A\bar{B} + AB(\bar{D} + \bar{C}), \\
&= A\bar{B} + AB\bar{D} + AB\bar{C}, \\
&= A(\bar{B} + B\bar{D}) + AB\bar{C}, \\
&= A(\bar{B} + \bar{D}) + AB\bar{C}, \\
&= A\bar{B} + A\bar{D} + AB\bar{C}, \\
&= A(\bar{B} + B\bar{C}) + A\bar{D}, \\
&= A(\bar{B} + \bar{C}) + A\bar{D}, \\
&= A\bar{B} + A\bar{C} + A\bar{D}.
\end{aligned}
$$

Thus, although algebra is the basis for all minimization, the direct use of the theorems is clumsy and often in doubt.

A mapping of this function requires 16 cells because it contains four variables. This is shown in Figure 3.17a. The mapping is accomplished by inserting a 1 in each cell for which the function is 1 and inserting a 0 in each cell where the function is 0. Inspection of the function reveals that it will be 1 if the term $A\bar{B}$ is 1. Thus, in each cell where A is 1 and B is 0, insert 1.

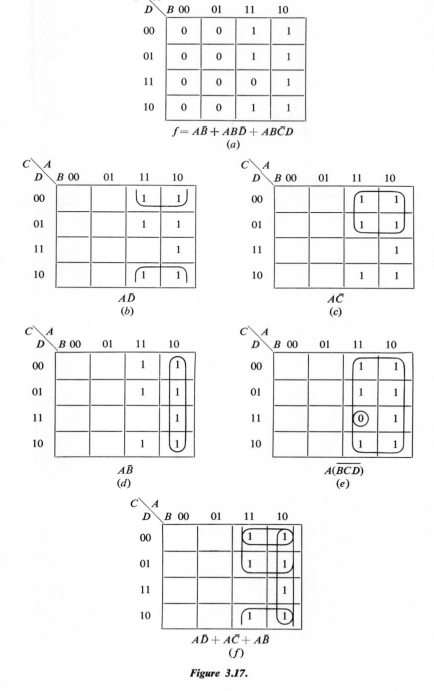

Figure 3.17.

This is the right-hand-most column and includes four cells. Next, the function is also 1 if the term $AB\bar{D}$ is 1. This covers two cells, the column where both A and B are 1 and the rows where D is 0. Finally, the function is 1 if the term $AB\bar{C}D$ is 1. This is the intersection of the column where A and B are both 1's and the row where C is 0 and D is 1. All remaining cells are 0.

Once the function is mapped, the next step is to group the 1's in such a way that a minimal expression results. This is shown in Figure 3.17*b–d.* Three separate groups, of four cells each, can be made to result in the terms $A\bar{D}$, $A\bar{C}$, and $A\bar{B}$. Another way of grouping the 1's in this expression to encircle those contained by A but *not* by the cell defined by B, C, and D. This will produce the factored form

$$f = A(\overline{BCD})$$
$$= A(\bar{B} + \bar{C} + \bar{D})$$

and is illustrated in Figure 3.17*e.*

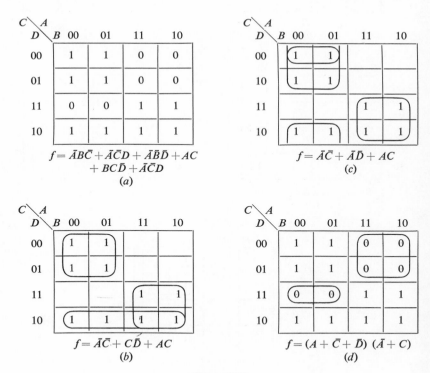

$$f = \bar{A}B\bar{C} + \bar{A}\bar{C}D + \bar{A}\bar{B}\bar{D} + AC$$
$$+ BC\bar{D} + \bar{A}\bar{C}D$$
(a)

$$f = \bar{A}\bar{C} + \bar{A}\bar{D} + AC$$
(c)

$$f = \bar{A}\bar{C} + C\bar{D} + AC$$
(b)

$$f = (A + \bar{C} + \bar{D})(\bar{A} + C)$$
(d)

Figure 3.18.

A little experience with this mapping technique will enable the student to map the function, accomplish the grouping, and write the minimal expression from inspection. It is not easy to assure oneself that the algebraic technique has truly resulted in a minimal form. However, it is easy to prove the existence of the minimal form or forms by inspection of the map. In addition, any and all possible forms can be written by inspection of the map. The map provides complete insight into the functions and all possible combinations.

EXAMPLE 3.2. *Minimize* $f = \bar{A}B\bar{C} + \bar{A}\bar{C}D + \bar{A}B\bar{D} + AC + BC\bar{D} + \bar{A}\bar{C}D.$

This is mapped in Figure 3.18a. Once it has been mapped the picture will generally reveal obvious patterns or groupings. Figure 3.18b shows one possible grouping that yields a valid function. Figure 3.18c, however, is another equally valid grouping. The ability to recognize these different groupings is quite important when implementing a function, as it could result in a cheaper network. Figure 3.18d groups the 0's. In this example the 0's can be written more quickly and without ambiguity, as there is only one minimal arrangement.

3.7 MULTIPLE MAPPING

It is not convenient to map more than a 5-bit function because it becomes too large and clumsy. Almost always, however, a particular sequence, combination, or grouping that is required lends itself to multiple mapping in such a way that only four of the variables, or fewer, need actually be mapped.

Multiple mapping involves the assignment of more than one state to each cell in a map. For example, a four-variable function contains 16 different combinations. Letting the four variables be A, B, C, and D with weight assignments of $D = 2^0 = 1$, $C = 2^1 = 2$, $B = 2^2 = 4$, and $A = 2^3 = 8$, it can be said that all the even numbers require $D = 0$ and all the odd numbers require $D = 1$. Also, all numbers below 8 are defined by $A = 0$ whereas all numbers of 8 and above are defined by $A = 1$. That is, the requirement that an output be provided whenever the numbers 9 and 11 occur indicates that A must be 1. If A must be 1 there is no need to map a 4-bit function, because the state of A is already determined and the only remaining requirement is to determine the combinational states of B, C, and D. This can be done as shown in Figure 3.19. Figure 3.19a shows a 3-bit map with a predetermined state of $A = 1$. This is equivalent to mapping only the right-hand portion of a 4-bit map. The cells within the map start off with the

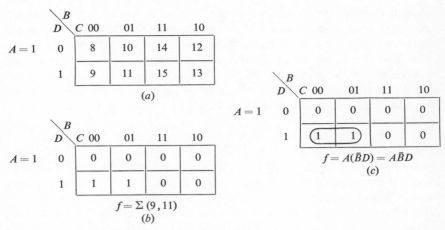

(a)

$f = \Sigma\,(9, 11)$
(b)

$f = A(\bar{B}D) = A\bar{B}D$
(c)

Figure 3.19.

assumption that $A = 1$; therefore the weights of the cells start at decimal 8 and go to decimal 15. Since the function desired is for decimal 9 and 11, a 1 is inserted in the appropriate cell and a minimal function is written. However, the one provision is that A has been predetermined to be 1. This predetermined condition must be AND'ed with the resulting term. This gives the function $f = A(\bar{B}D) = A\bar{B}D$.

EXAMPLE 3.4. Suppose the requirement is to provide an output whenever any number from 4 through 11 occurs. This is a simple requirement but is used here for illustration. A 4-bit map could be used, but a 3-bit map will

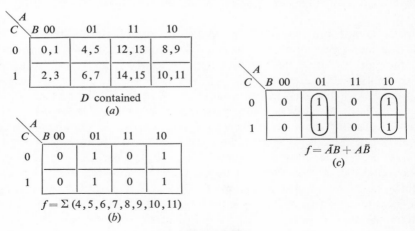

D contained
(a)

$f = \Sigma\,(4, 5, 6, 7, 8, 9, 10, 11)$
(b)

$f = \bar{A}B + A\bar{B}$
(c)

Figure 3.20.

be used to show how it is done. This example requires a 3-bit map with the least significant variable contained. That is, consistent with the usual notations for a four-variable function where $A = 2^3 = 8$, $B = 2^2 = 4$, $C = 2^1 = 2$, and $D = 2^0 = 1$, the inclusion of the least significant bit, D, in each cell implies that each cell must include two states. Referring to Figure 3.20a, the first cell relates to $\bar{A}\bar{B}\bar{C}$ and, because D is included for all possible combinations of D, it must contain the decimal states of 0 and 1 for the states of $D = 0$ and $D = 1$. This is equivalent to making each cell in this 3-bit map look as if it contained two finite cells within each major cell. In fact this is exactly what is happening. Each cell contains a finite combination for the variables A, B, and C. But they must include the possibilities of D being 0 and 1. Thus the mapping for the function $f = \Sigma(4,5,6,7,8,9,10,11)$ is shown in Figure 3.20b. A 1 is contained in the cell representing 4 and 5, in the cell representing 6 and 7, in the cell representing 8 and 9, and in the cell representing 10 and 11. Figure 3.20c shows the grouping for writing the minimal expression. It is convenient in this example that the number group required is independent of D in such a way that D is not prime to the solution.

EXAMPLE 3.5. Suppose this were not true; that is, suppose it were desired to provide a 1 output for the function

$$f = \Sigma(4,5,6,7,8,9,10).$$

This could be mapped with a 4-bit variable map, but—just to be stubborn— it will be illustrated with a 3-bit map. This can be handled as shown in Figure 3.21. The fact that a cell is not to be fully completed is noted. This

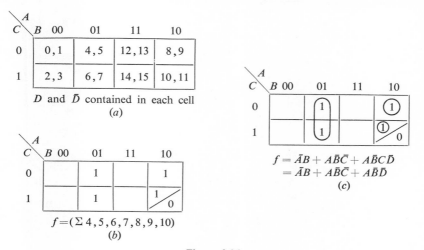

D and $\bar{D}$ contained in each cell

(a)

$f = (\Sigma\, 4,5,6,7,8,9,10)$

(b)

$f = \bar{A}B + A\bar{B}\bar{C} + A\bar{B}C\bar{D}$
$\quad = \bar{A}B + A\bar{B}\bar{C} + A\bar{B}\bar{D}$

(c)

Figure 3.21.

means that it is a special case. The grouping for 4, 5, 6, and 7 can be made as before and yields the function $\bar{A}B$. However, since the count of 11 is not contained in the requirements, the grouping of 8, 9, 10, and 11 cannot be made this time. But the single 1 for the cell containing 8 and 9 can be written as $A\bar{B}\bar{C}$ and the special case of 10 can be written in its cannonic form of $A\bar{B}C\bar{D}$, giving the total expression

$$f = \bar{A}B + A\bar{B}\bar{C} + A\bar{B}C\bar{D}.$$

An examination of this expression indicates that C is not required in the last term because $A\bar{B}(\bar{C} + C\bar{D}) = A\bar{B}(\bar{C} + \bar{D})$. This gives the final expression

$$f = \bar{A}B + A\bar{B}\bar{C} + A\bar{B}\bar{D}.$$

This reduction may seem a reversion to algebra and is just that. As is often the case in large, complex functions, without the use of special devices the algebraic theorems are still the fundamental tool in minimization.

However, do not give up yet. There is another approach to handling problems of this type. That is, break the problem into two separate problems, such as

$$f = \Sigma(4,5,6,7) + \Sigma(8,9,10).$$

This automatically reduces the problem into two 3-bit problems by determining that $A = 0$ for the number digits 4, 5, 6, and 7 whereas $A = 1$ for the number digits 8, 9, and 10. Figure 3.22 shows two different 3-bit maps.

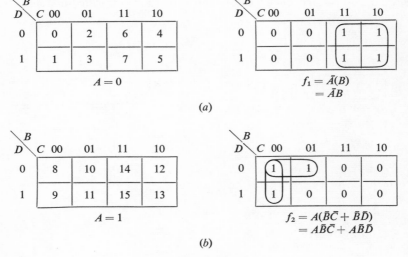

Figure 3.22.

Figure 3.22*a* is a 3-bit map with $A = 0$ so that it contains the number digits 0, 1, 2, 3, 4, 5, 6, and 7. Thus, if f_1 is defined as the first part of the problem, then $f_1 = \bar{A}(B)$ or $f_1 = \bar{A}B$. The second part of the problem relates to the number digits 8, 9, and 10, which require that $A = 1$. Figure 3.22*b* is a map of the three variables B, C, and D with $A = 1$. This can be defined as f_2, where f_2 accounts for the number digits 8, 9, and 10. Therefore a minimal function for f_2 is $f_2 = A(\bar{B}\bar{C} + \bar{B}\bar{D})$. The sum of f_1 and f_2 will fulfill the requirements of the problem.

$$f = f_1 + f_2$$
$$= \bar{A}B + A\bar{B}\bar{C} + A\bar{B}\bar{D}.$$

EXAMPLE 3.6. This approach can be applied to larger and more complex problems. For example, given a 5-bit function, provide an output whenever the magnitude of the 5 bits is equal to or greater than 21. Figure 3.23*a* shows a 4-bit map where the most significant bit, A, is contained as 1. That is, by defining the variables as

$$\begin{array}{ccccc} A & B & C & D & E \quad \text{(variable)} \\ 16 & 8 & 4 & 2 & 1 \quad \text{(weight),} \end{array}$$

a map of the 4 lower-order bits must start at decimal 16 and progress to 31. Thus any expression written from this map must contain the variable A. Figure 3.23*b* is an analysis of the problem and a minimal expression that results from a proper grouping of the 1's. Thus a 5-bit requirement has been analyzed with a 4-bit map. An exercise left to the reader will be to separate this problem into two separate problems by defining the required function as

$$f = \Sigma(21 \to 23) + \Sigma(24 \to 31)$$

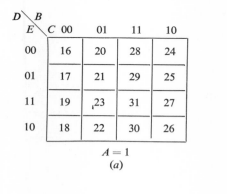

$A = 1$

(*a*)

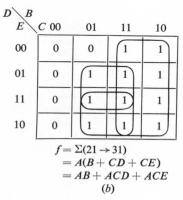

$f = \Sigma(21 \to 31)$
$= A(B + CD + CE)$
$= AB + ACD + ACE$

(*b*)

Figure 3.23.

and accomplishing the mapping with two 3-bit maps. One final note before leaving this last example: notice in Figure 3.23b that the grouping of the 1's requires writing three separate terms, whereas a grouping of the 0's would require only two terms. A function based on the grouping of the 0's would be written as

$$f = A[(B + C)(B + D + E)].$$

EXAMPLE 3.7. Another example, involving a slightly more complex requirement, would be to provide a 1 output for the decimal numbers 24 through 63 inclusive from a 7-bit word input. Seven bits contain 2^7 or 128 different possible combinations. An assignment of the variables to a 7-bit function can be made as shown:

$$A \quad B \quad C \quad D \quad E \quad F \quad G \quad \text{(variable)}$$
$$64 \quad 32 \quad 16 \quad 8 \quad 4 \quad 2 \quad 1 \quad \text{(weight)}.$$

The required function is $f = \Sigma(24 \to 63)$. Because the required function does not exceed 63 it is known that A must be 0. For, if $A = 1$, the magnitude of the function is greater than 63. Therefore A is not necessary in the mapping. This reduces the requirements to 6 bits.

The lowest decimal number required is 24, which is arrived at when C and D $(16 + 8)$ are 1's. Thus D is the least-order bit that should be of concern, and a mapping of the bits B, C, and D should be sufficient, as shown in Figure 3.24. Each cell of the map in Figure 3.24a contains the variables E, F, and G. Because the collective weight of these lower order bits is 8 each cell in the map must contain the equivalent of all possible combinations of E, F, and G. This is implied when the decimal designation of the first cell contains the numbers 0 through 7, the second cell contains the numbers 8 through 15, and so on. Thus, for $A = 0$, the 3-bit map shown accommodates the required function. Figure 3.24b shows the mapping and the grouping of the 1's to yield the function

$$f = \bar{A}B + \bar{A}CD.$$

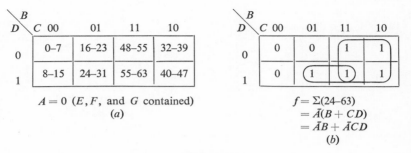

A = 0 (E, F, and G contained)
(a)

$$f = \Sigma(24\text{–}63)$$
$$= \bar{A}(B + CD)$$
$$= \bar{A}B + \bar{A}CD$$
(b)

Figure 3.24.

The previous example indicates again how a single cell can contain a group of events. In that case the least significant bit mapped was D, which had a weight of 8. Therefore any time D goes from 0 to 1 the weight of the cell should be increased by 8. This is what was mapped. It could also be stated that each cell in Figure 3.24a contains an eight-cell map or matrix representing all the possible states of the lower order bits E, F, and G.

EXAMPLE 3.8. *Analyze and minimize* $f = \Sigma(10, 12, 14, 20, 22)$.

One approach to the problem is the straightforward mapping of the function in a 5-bit map as shown in Figure 3.25a and b. The map indicates that three four-literal terms are required to express the function.

An alternative approach is to recognize that the function is composed of all even terms. This implies that the least significant bit, E, must be 0 for any of the parts. Thus a 4-bit map will suffice when E is always held at 0. Figure 3.26a and b illustrates this approach.

Still another approach is to divide the function into two parts. One grouping could contain the numbers below 16 while the second grouping would contain the numbers 16 and above.

$$f = \Sigma(10, 12, 14) + \Sigma(20, 22)$$
$$= f_1 + f_2 .$$

$D \backslash B$				
$E \backslash C$	00	01	11	10
0 00	0	4	12	8
0 01	1	5	13	9
$\bar{A}$ 0 11	3	7	15	11
0 10	2	6	14	10
1 10	18	22	30	26
1 11	19	23	31	27
A 1 01	17	21	29	25
1 00	16	20	28	24

A B C D E (variable)
16   8   4   2   1 (weight)
(a)

$f = \Sigma(10, 12, 14, 20, 22)$
$= \bar{A}BC\bar{E} + \bar{A}BD\bar{E} + A\bar{B}C\bar{E}$
(b)

Figure 3.25.

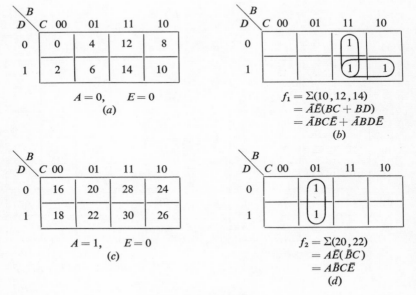

C\A D\B	00	01	11	10
00	0	8	24	16
01	2	10	26	18
11	6	14	30	22
10	4	12	28	20

$E = 0$
5-bit function
(a)

$f = \Sigma(10, 12, 14, 20, 22)$
$= \bar{E}(\bar{A}BD + \bar{A}BC + A\bar{B}C)$
$= \bar{A}BD\bar{E} + \bar{A}BC\bar{E} + A\bar{B}C\bar{E}$
(b)

Figure 3.26.

Because f_1 contains only even numbers below 16, a 3-bit map would suffice as shown in Figure 3.27a and b. Figure 3.27c and d shows the mapping of f_2 as a 3-bit function for 16 and above. The summation of f_1 and f_2 completes the solution.

$$f = f_1 + f_2$$
$$= \bar{A}BC\bar{E} + \bar{A}BD\bar{E} + A\bar{B}C\bar{E}$$

D\C	00	01	11	10
0	0	4	12	8
1	2	6	14	10

$A = 0, \quad E = 0$
(a)

$f_1 = \Sigma(10, 12, 14)$
$= \bar{A}\bar{E}(BC + BD)$
$= \bar{A}BC\bar{E} + \bar{A}BD\bar{E}$
(b)

D\C	00	01	11	10
0	16	20	28	24
1	18	22	30	26

$A = 1, \quad E = 0$
(c)

$f_2 = \Sigma(20, 22)$
$= A\bar{E}(\bar{B}C)$
$= A\bar{B}C\bar{E}$
(d)

Figure 3.27.

3.8   QUINE-McCLUSKEY METHOD

The Quine-McCluskey (QM) method is a systematic approach to obtaining minimal expressions when a large number of variables are involved and is of considerable use in multifunctional problems. It is an approach that can be programmed in a computer and is thus of great interest in special large problems.

Essentially the QM method consists of repeated applications of the theorem $XY + \bar{X}Y = Y$. For example, the expression $ABC + \bar{A}BC$ can be reduced to BC by recognizing that A and $\bar{A}$ are the only differences between the two terms. In a like manner the expression $\bar{A}B\bar{C}D + \bar{A}\bar{B}\bar{C}D$ can be reduced to $\bar{A}\bar{C}D$ by recognizing that B is redundant. This is the essence of the technique. Just as the Karnaugh map has only a one-variable change between adjacent cells, the QM method systematically searches for a one-variable difference between terms.

The first step in applying the QM method is to expand the function into a standard sum form of canonical terms. Actually, rather than expanding the function in a standard sum form, a listing is made of all the canonical terms in a table.

EXAMPLE 3.9. $f = \bar{A}B\bar{C} + \bar{A}BD + A\bar{B}\bar{C} + A\bar{B}D + \bar{A}BC$.

Assume the weight assignments previously used of $A = 8$, $B = 4$, $C = 2$, $D = 1$; then Table 3.1 will contain all the canonical terms for the above function in algebra, binary, and decimal. The reason for this will become obvious as the examples are explained. The next step is to compare each canonical term with every other canonical term, looking for a one-variable difference. That is, the first term, $\bar{A}B\bar{C}D$, compares with the second term, $\bar{A}B\bar{C}\bar{D}$, with the D variable being redundant. Because these two terms will reduce to $\bar{A}B\bar{C}$, a three-variable term, this is listed in a new table, Table 3.2, and a check mark is placed alongside each of the two terms to show that they have been used in a reduction. Notice that the binary representation differed only in one variable, and this is identified in Table 3.2 by placing a dash in this position. Furthermore, this comparison was between a decimal 5 and a decimal 4; this is a difference of a decimal 1, which is a binary multiple ($2^0 = 1$).

The next term that compares with $\bar{A}B\bar{C}D$ is the third term $\bar{A}BCD$. This produces the second term in Table 3.2, $\bar{A}BD$. A check mark is placed beside the $\bar{A}BCD$ term in Table 3.1, and the reduced term is listed in Table 3.2. This time C is the redundant variable and a dash is placed in the position C normally occupies. Furthermore, the decimal difference between these terms is 2, a power of 2 ($2^1 = 2$), which is the weight of the variable C. No further

TABLE 3.1

Canonical terms	Binary	Decimal
$\bar{A}B\bar{C}D$ √	0 1 0 1	(5)
$\bar{A}B\bar{C}\bar{D}$ √	0 1 0 0	(4)
$\bar{A}BCD$ √	0 1 1 1	(7)
$A\bar{B}\bar{C}D$ √	1 0 0 1	(9)
$A\bar{B}\bar{C}\bar{D}$ √	1 0 0 0	(8)
$A\bar{B}CD$ √	1 0 1 1	(11)
$\bar{A}BC\bar{D}$ √	0 1 1 0	(6)

TABLE 3.2

Algebra	Binary	Decimal
$\bar{A}B\bar{C}$ √	0 1 0 –	(4,5)
$\bar{A}BD$ √	0 1 – 1	(5,7)
$\bar{A}B\bar{D}$ √	0 1 – 0	(4,6)
$\bar{A}BC$ √	0 1 1 –	(6,7)
$A\bar{B}D$ *	1 0 – 1	(9,11)
$A\bar{B}\bar{C}$ *	1 0 0 –	(8,9)

comparisons can be made with the first term. The second term is now compared with each term below it, and a check mark is placed beside each term that compares according to the rule. Only one term develops, $\bar{A}B\bar{D}$. The process continues with the third term in Table 3.1. The third term, $\bar{A}BCD$, compares with the last term, $\bar{A}BC\bar{D}$, to produce $\bar{A}BC$. The process continues until all possible comparisons have been made. In this example Table 3.1 has been completely checked off and will be of no further use. The comparison process now continues with Table 3.2. Each term in Table 3.2 is compared with every other term of Table 3.2 in an effort to eliminate redundant variables. The first term, $\bar{A}B\bar{C}$, compares with $\bar{A}BC$ to eliminate the C variable. Table 3.3 now lists these comparisons. The binary form now contains two dashes, one for the C variable and one for the D variable. In addition, the decimal part contains the numbers represented by the binary form with all possible combinations. Thus $\bar{A}$ B – – has 0 for A and 1 for B, giving decimal 4. The two dashes represent a possible magnitude of 3; therefore the decimal part shows that the term $\bar{A}B$ represents and contains the decimal numbers 4, 5, 6, and 7.

The next term in Table 3.2, $\bar{A}BD$, compares with $\bar{A}B\bar{D}$ to eliminate $\bar{D}$. This results in the term $\bar{A}B$. But $\bar{A}B$ is already represented, and so it is not necessary to list it twice. This process repeats just as before until all possible comparisons have been made. In this case no further comparisons can be made.

The next step is to create a table with all the original canonical terms across the top and all prime implicants in a column at the left of the table. This is called the prime implicant table (Table 3.4). The prime implicants

TABLE 3.3

Algebra	Binary	Decimal
$\bar{A}B$ *	0 1 – –	(4,5,6,7)

TABLE 3.4 Prime Implicant Table

Prime implicant		$\bar{A}B\bar{C}D$ 0 1 0 1 (5)	$\bar{A}B\bar{C}\bar{D}$ 0 1 0 0 (4)	$\bar{A}BCD$ 0 1 1 1 (7)	$A\bar{B}\bar{C}D$ 1 0 0 1 (9)	$A\bar{B}\bar{C}\bar{D}$ 1 0 0 0 (8)	$A\bar{B}CD$ 1 0 1 1 (11)	$\bar{A}BC\bar{D}$ 0 1 1 0 (6)
						Canonical terms		
(9, 11)	$A\bar{B}D$				×		⊗	
(8, 9)	$A\bar{B}\bar{C}$				×	⊗		
(4, 5, 6, 7)	$\bar{A}B$	⊗	⊗	⊗				⊗

$$f = \bar{A}B + A\bar{B}\bar{C} + A\bar{B}D$$

are any terms in any of the tables that did not compare with another term. An asterisk is placed beside these terms in the table to identify them. Next a × is placed in the table under each canonical term in the row of the prime implicant that contains that term. That is, $A\bar{B}D$ contains the canonical terms $A\bar{B}CD$ and $A\bar{B}\bar{C}D$. These are also identified as decimal 9 and 11. The prime implicant $A\bar{B}\bar{C}$ contains the terms for decimal 8 and 9. Finally, the prime implicant $\bar{A}B$ contains the terms for 4, 5, 6, and 7. Each and every canonical term must be contained, because these are the original terms. Any canonical term that is contained by only one prime implicant identifies that prime implicant as an *essential* prime implicant. This means that it is necessary for the problem. A circle is placed around the × to identify the prime implicant as essential. The summation of the essential prime implicants along with any others necessary to contain all the canonical terms is a final solution. Thus the solution to this problem is

$$f = \bar{A}B + A\bar{B}\bar{C} + A\bar{B}D,$$

because in this example all of the prime implicants are essential.

It can be seen that working with decimal numbers can be quite efficient. This is accomplished by utilizing the following steps:

1. List all the decimal numbers contained within each term of the original expression.

2. Arrange the first table in groups containing equal numbers of 1; that is, all terms containing no 1's, followed by all terms containing one 1, followed by all terms containing two 1's, and so on.

3. Compare each term of one group with each term of the group below it, looking for a single 1 difference. List all comparisons in another table and check off compared terms. Continue this process, creating new tables, until all comparisons have been made.

4. Identify the prime implicant terms.

5. Set up a prime implicant table and identify essential prime implicants.

6. Select appropriate prime implicants to create a minimal expression or expressions.

EXAMPLE 3.10. A study of the example in Tables 3.5 through 3.9 will illustrate the technique. The first step is to convert the algebraic expression into its decimal equivalent. This is the same as expanding the terms into canonical terms. The term $\bar{A}\bar{B}C\bar{E}$ can be expanded by $\bar{A}\bar{B}C\bar{E}(D + \bar{D}) = \bar{A}\bar{B}CDE + \bar{A}\bar{B}C\bar{D}E$. This represents $00010 + 00000$. Instead of expanding, a ϕ is written for each missing term to indicate that this term is present as a 1 as well as a 0. Thus the term $\bar{A}\bar{B}C\bar{E}$ is written as $000\phi0$, which implies 00010 and 00000. The decimal contents of this term are therefore 0 and 2. That is, since D has a weight of $2^1 = 2$ and its magnitude is 0 in one case and 1 in the other, the magnitude of the term $000\phi0$ is 0 as well as 2.

EXAMPLE 3.10. $f = \overline{A}\overline{B}\overline{C}\overline{E} + B\overline{C}D + \overline{A}B\overline{C}\overline{E} + A\overline{B}CDE + AC\overline{D}\overline{E}$
$\qquad\qquad + ABCE + A\overline{B}CE + AC\overline{E}.$

Assume weight assignments of $A = 16$, $B = 8$, $C = 4$, $D = 2$, and $E = 1$.

$f = 0 \quad 0 \quad 0 \quad \phi \quad 0 + \phi \quad 1 \quad 0 \quad 1 \quad \phi + 0 \quad 1 \quad 0 \quad \phi \quad 0 + 1 \quad 0 \quad 1 \quad 1 \quad 1$
$\qquad (0,2) \qquad\qquad (10,11,26,27) \qquad\qquad (8,10) \qquad\qquad\qquad (23)$

$\quad + 1 \quad \phi \quad 1 \quad 0 \quad 0 + 1 \quad 1 \quad 1 \quad \phi \quad 1 + 1 \quad 0 \quad 1 \quad \phi \quad i + 1 \quad \phi \quad 1 \quad \phi \quad 0$
$\qquad (20,28) \qquad\qquad (29,31) \qquad\qquad (21,23) \qquad\qquad (20,22,28,30)$

$= \Sigma(0,2,8,10,11,20,21,22,23,26,27,28,29,30,31).$

The second term, $B\overline{C}D$, has two variables missing. A canonical expansion of this term will be A and $\overline{A}$ as well as E and $\overline{E}$. Therefore, it may be expressed as $\phi 101\phi$. The decimal combinations contained in this expression are $0 + 8 + 0 + 2 + 0 = 10$, $0 + 8 + 0 + 2 + 1$, $16 + 8 + 0 + 2 + 0$, and $16 + 8 + 0 + 2 + 1$, or 10, 11, 26, and 27. These combinations are shown under each term in the example. The numbers are then collected in proper numerical sequence.

Table 3.5 lists all the numbers according to the number of 1's. This is because the object is to find differences of only one variable. Thus there is no reason to compare a number containing one 1 with a number containing three 1's. This avoids unnecessary comparisons. Comparisons in Table 3.5 are made among groups. The first group, of no 1's, compares with all terms in the second group. These comparisons are checked off and form the first group of Table 3.6. The decimal numbers are noted. Comparison with each subsequent group continues until all comparisons have been made. The terms in the group of one 1 will compare with terms in the group of two 1's provided there is a binary multiple difference. Therefore decimal 2 will compare with decimal 10 to provide the redundant 8. But 2 will not compare with decimal 20. The comparison of 2 and 10 produces the term 0–010, with a dash in the position representing the weight of 8. Any time that a comparison has already been contained in a previous comparison it may be checked off as having been compared. Table 3.6 therefore represents the removal of one variable. The variable that has been removed is always identified as the difference of the decimal numbers. This is also apparent in Example 3.1. All terms in Table 3.5 can be compared; thus there are no prime implicants in Table 3.5. Similarly, all terms in Table 3.6 can be compared; thus there are no prime implicants in Table 3.5.

Table 3.7 is a comparison of terms from Table 3.6. This table reflects the elimination of two variables. An asterisk is placed beside terms that cannot be contained in a comparison. These are prime implicants and

TABLE 3.5

No 1's	0	0	0	0	0	(0)√
One 1's	0	0	0	1	0	(2)√
	0	1	0	0	0	(8)√
Two 1's	0	1	0	1	0	(10√
	1	0	1	0	0	(20)√
Three 1's	0	1	0	1	1	(11)√
	1	0	1	0	1	(21)√
	1	0	1	1	0	(22)√
	1	1	0	1	0	(26)√
	1	1	1	0	0	(28)√
Four 1's	1	0	1	1	1	(23)√
	1	1	0	1	1	(27)√
	1	1	1	0	1	(29)√
	1	1	1	1	0	(30)√
Five 1's	1	1	1	1	1	(31)√

TABLE 3.6

0	0	0	–	0	(0,2)√
0	–	0	0	0	(0,8)√
0	–	0	1	0	(2,10)√
0	1	0	–	0	(8,10)√
0	1	0	1	–	(10,11)√
–	1	0	1	0	(10,26)√
1	0	1	0	–	(20,21)√
1	0	1	–	0	(20,22)√
1	–	1	0	0	(20,28)√
–	1	0	1	1	(11,27)√
1	0	1	–	1	(21,23)√
1	–	1	0	1	(21,29)√
1	0	1	1	–	(22,23)√
1	–	1	1	0	(22,30)√
1	1	0	1	–	(26,27)√
1	1	–	1	0	(26,30)√
1	1	1	0	–	(28,29)√
1	1	1	–	0	(28,30)√
1	–	1	1	1	(23,31)√
1	1	–	1	1	(27,31)√
1	1	1	–	1	(29,31)√
1	1	1	1	–	(30,31)√

TABLE 3.7

0	–	0	–	0	(0,2,8,10) *(a)
–	1	0	1	–	(10,11,26,27) *(b)
1	0	1	–	–	(20,21,22,23)√
1	0	1	0	–	(20,21,28,29)√
1	–	1	–	0	(20,22,28,30)√
1	–	1	–	1	(21,23,29,31)√
1	–	1	1	–	(22,23,30,31)√
1	1	–	1	–	(26,27,30,31) *(c)
1	1	1	–	–	(28,29,30,31)√

TABLE 3.8

1	–	1	–	–	(20,21,22,23,28, 29,30,31) *(d)

are further identified by the letters *a*, *b*, and *c*. There is only one term in Table 3.8, and it must therefore be a prime implicant.

The prime implicant table (Table 3.9) is prepared as before, except that the column headings are the decimal numbers rather than their algebraic equivalents. The prime implicants *a*, *b*, *c*, and *d* are listed, and a × is placed

TABLE 3.9 Prime Implicant Table

	0	2	8	10	11	20	21	22	23	26	27	28	29	30	31	
0,2,8,10	⊗	⊗	⊗	×												(a)*
10,11,26,27				×	⊗					×	×					(b)*
26,27,30,31										×	×			×	×	(c)
20,21,22,23,						⊗	⊗	⊗	⊗							
28,29,30,31												⊗	⊗	×	×	(d)*

$(a)^* = (0,2,8,10) = 0 \ - \ 0 \ - \ 0 = \bar{A}\bar{C}\bar{E}$

$(b)^* = (10,11,26,27) = - \ 1 \ 0 \ 1 \ - = B\bar{C}D$

$(d)^* = (20,21,22,23,28,29,30,31) = 1 \ - \ 1 \ - \ - = AC$

$\therefore \ f = \bar{A}\bar{C}\bar{E} + B\bar{C}D + AC.$

in the appropriate columns. Any number that is contained in only one prime implicant is noted by placing a circle around the × and placing an asterisk beside the letter identifying that particular prime implicant. These are the essential prime implicants. They are required for the solution, because all numbers across the top of the table must be included in any solution. There are three essential prime implicants in this particular problem: *a*, *b*, and *d*. The sum of these prime implicants represents a minimal expression.

PROBLEMS

1. Minimize, using truth table or map:
   (a) $f = AB\bar{C}D + ABC\bar{D} + B\bar{C}D + \bar{A}BC\bar{D}.$
   (b) $f = \bar{A}\bar{B}C\bar{D} + \bar{A}C\bar{D} + ABC\bar{D} + \bar{A}\bar{B}CD.$
   (c) $f = ABC + BC + A\bar{B}C.$
   (d) $f = A\bar{C} + AB + BC.$
   (e) $f = AB\bar{C} + \bar{A}\bar{B}\bar{C} + A\bar{B}\bar{C} + \bar{A}B\bar{C}.$
   (f) $f = B\bar{C}\bar{D} + A\bar{C}\bar{D} + ABC\bar{D} + A\bar{B}\bar{C}D.$
   (g) $f = (A + B + \bar{C})(\bar{A} + B + \bar{C}).$
   (h) $f = C(A\bar{B} + AB\bar{D} + A\bar{B}D) + A\bar{C}.$
2. Prove the following equalities, using truth table or map:
   (a) $\bar{A}\bar{B}C + A\bar{B}\bar{C} + \bar{A}B\bar{C} + A\bar{B}C = (\bar{B} + C)(\bar{B} + \bar{C}).$
   (b) $A\bar{C} + A\bar{B} + AC\bar{D} = (A + B)(A + \bar{B})(\bar{B} + \bar{C} + \bar{D}).$
   (c) $ABC + (\bar{A} + \bar{B})D = (AB + D)(\bar{A} + \bar{B} + C).$
   (d) $A\bar{C}\bar{D} + A\bar{B}D + AC\bar{D} = A(\bar{B} + \bar{D}).$
3. Minimize the following functions, using the map technique:
   (a) $f = \Sigma (0,5,10,15) + \Sigma_\phi (1,7,11,13).$
   (b) $f = \Sigma (5,6,8,9,12,13,14).$
   (c) $f = \Sigma (0,4,5,6,7,10,11).$
   (d) $f = \Sigma (0,1,4,5,8,9) + \Sigma_\phi (7,10,12,13).$

4. Write a minimal expression for the following maps:

C \ A, B	00	01	11	10
0	1	0	1	1
1	0	1	1	1

(a)

C \ A, B	00	01	11	10
0	1	0	0	0
1	1	1	0	1

(b)

C \ A, B	00	01	11	10
0	1	1	1	0
1	0	0	1	1

(c)

C,D \ A,B	00	01	11	10
00	0	0	1	0
01	0	1	1	1
11	0	0	0	1
10	0	0	0	1

(d)

C,D \ A,B	00	01	11	10
00	0	1	1	0
01	0	1	0	0
11	0	1	0	0
10	0	1	1	0

(e)

C,D \ A,B	00	01	11	10
00	1	1	0	1
01	0	0	0	0
11	0	0	0	0
10	1	0	1	1

(f)

C,D \ A,B	00	01	11	10
00	0	0	1	0
01	1	1	ϕ	ϕ
11	0	ϕ	ϕ	1
10	0	0	1	0

(g)

C,D \ A,B	00	01	11	10
00	1	0	1	ϕ
01	1	0	1	0
11	ϕ	ϕ	0	0
10	ϕ	0	0	ϕ

(h)

$C \backslash A$ $D \backslash B$	00	01	11	10
00	0	ϕ	1	0
01	0	0	1	ϕ
11	0	ϕ	1	ϕ
10	ϕ	0	0	0

(i)

$C \backslash A$ $D \backslash B$	00	01	11	10
00	0	1	1	0
01	0	1	1	0
11	0	0	0	0
10	0	1	1	0

(j)

$C \backslash A$ $D \backslash B$	00	01	11	10
00	1	0	0	1
01	1	0	0	0
11	1	0	0	0
10	1	0	0	1

(k)

$C \backslash A$ $D \backslash B$	00	01	11	10
00	0	1	1	0
01	1	0	0	1
11	1	0	0	1
10	0	1	1	0

(l)

$C \backslash A$ $D \backslash B$	00	01	11	10
00	0	0	0	1
01	0	1	1	1
11	1	1	0	0
10	1	0	0	0

(m)

$C \backslash A$ $D \backslash B$	00	01	11	10
00	0	0	0	0
01	1	1	1	1
11	0	0	0	0
10	1	1	1	1

(n)

$C \backslash A$ $D \backslash B$	00	01	11	10
00	0	1	ϕ	0
01	0	1	ϕ	0
11	0	ϕ	1	0
10	0	0	1	ϕ

(o)

4

DIGITAL INTEGRATED CIRCUITS

4.1 INTRODUCTION

The previous chapters have set the stage for logic design by providing the fundamental tools used by the logic designer. Number systems and Boolean algebra are basic. Minimization procedures are fairly well established but still leave much to the skill, technique, and experience of the individual designer. Before launching into the field of analysis, synthesis, and implementation it seems appropriate to discuss the hardware that will be used in this text—digital integrated circuits.

It is true that logic design can be taught entirely from logic symbols without reference to or concern with their physical implementation. But this is intended to be a practical book to be used by the practicing engineer. The problems at the end of the chapters are designed to be solved with actual integrated circuits so that practical experience is gained not only in logic design but in the use of actual hardware. The assignments should be done with a particular logic family for each problem or group of problems. This can be accomplished if summary-type data sheets on several different logic families are made available to the student as a guide. These summary sheets need only contain such information as gate types, part numbers, fan-out, propagation delay, and power.

Some basic definitions, conventions, and logic symbols are necessary for an understanding of the material in this text. These definitions and conventions are well established and accepted throughout industry. The logic symbols used are taken from MIL-STD-806B.

Definitions

Digital: a number, a digit.

Logic: the science of the formal principles of reasoning; for example, digital logic is the science of reasoning with numbers.

Logic symbol: the graphical representation of the parts implementing a logic function.

Logic function: a combinational, storage, delay, or sequential function expressing a relationship between variable signal input(s) to a system or device and the resultant output(s).

Basic logic diagram: a logic diagram that depicts logic functions with no reference to physical implementation. It consists primarily of logic symbols and is used to depict all logic relationships as simply and understandably as possible. Nonlogic functions are not normally shown.

Detailed logic diagram: a diagram that depicts all logic functions and also shows nonlogic functions, socket locations, pin numbers, test points, and other physical elements necessary to describe the physical and electrical aspects of the logic.

Table of combinations: table describing the active input/output of the basic logic functions [i.e., HIGH (H) = more positive and LOW (L) = relatively less positive]. These functions are often written with 1's and 0's when properly defined.

Assignment of Logic Levels

Consider a device such as shown in Figure 4.1, whose active output (F) is a function of two input signals, A and B. The output and both input levels are capable of assuming only the arbitrarily chosen values of $+3$ V (HIGH, H) and -2 V (LOW, L). The circuit behaves according to Table 4.1.

The entries in Table 4.2 conform to the definition established for the table of combinations. These result when the mnemonic abbreviation H is substituted for $+3$ V and L for -2 V.

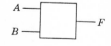

Figure 4.1 Logic device.

A table of combinations, or truth table, occurs when Boolean logic notations of 1 and 0 are assigned to the mnemonic H and L abbreviations or to the $+3$ V and -2 V electrical levels.

Positive logic, by definition, occurs when a 1 is assigned to represent the more positive level H, or $+3$ V, and a 0 is assigned to represent the less

TABLE 4.1 Level States		
Input		Output
A	B	F
−2 V	−2 V	−2 V
−2 V	+3 V	−2 V
+3 V	−2 V	−2 V
+3 V	+3 V	+3 V

TABLE 4.2 Table of Combinations		
Input		Output
A	B	F
L	L	L
L	H	L
H	L	L
H	H	H

positive level L, or − 2 V. Table 4.3 represents this logic state assignment and characterizes the AND gate of Figure 4.2.

Negative logic, by definition, occurs when a 0 is assigned to represent the more positive level H, or +3 V, and a 1 is assigned to represent the less positive level L, or − 2 V. Table 4.4 represents this logic state assignment and characterizes the OR gate of Figure 4.3.

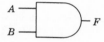

Figure 4.2   AND gate.

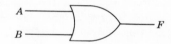

Figure 4.3   OR gate.

Note that Table 4.1, "Level States," and Table 4.2, "Table of Combinations," have not changed; only the assignment of the logic states 1 and 0 has been changed, which results in the need for two different logic symbols to represent the same device. Positive logic assignment to the high and low combinations result in an AND gate, whereas negative logic assignments result in an OR gate.

TABLE 4.3 Table of Combinations: Positive Logic		
Input		Output
A	B	F
0	0	0
0	1	0
1	0	0
1	1	1

TABLE 4.4 Table of Combinations: Negative Logic		
Input		Output
A	B	F
1	1	1
1	0	1
0	1	1
0	0	0

Basic Logic Symbols (Positive Logic)

AND: The symbol shown below represents the AND function. The AND output is high if and only if all the inputs are high.

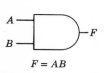

$$F = AB$$

Input		Output
A	B	F
0	0	0
0	1	0
1	0	0
1	1	1

OR: The symbol shown below represents the INCLUSIVE OR function. The OR output is low if and only if all inputs are low.

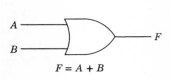

$$F = A + B$$

Input		Output
A	B	F
0	0	0
0	1	1
1	0	1
1	1	1

NAND: The NAND symbol is shown below and characterizes a function whose output is low (0) if and only if all inputs are high.

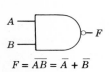

$$F = \overline{AB} = \overline{A} + \overline{B}$$

Input		Output
A	B	F
0	0	1
0	1	1
1	0	1
1	1	0

NOR: The NOR symbol is shown below and characterizes a function whose output is high if and only if all inputs are low.

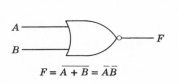

$$F = \overline{A + B} = \overline{A}\,\overline{B}$$

Input		Output
A	B	F
0	0	1
0	1	0
1	0	0
1	1	0

INVERTER: The inverter, shown below, is a device that provides the complement.

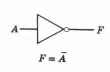

$$F = \overline{A}$$

Input	Output
A	F
0	1
1	0

General logic symbol: This is a symbol for functions not elsewhere specified. The symbol should be adequately labeled to identify the function performed. The flip-flop, single shot, and register are examples of the use of this symbol.

4.2 INTEGRATED CIRCUITS

There are four basic types of logic circuit configuration that have evolved into integrated circuit form. These are shown in Figures 4.4 through 4.7 as DCTL, DTL, T²L, and CML. Almost all of the available monolithic logic can be identified as some variation of one of these four types, even though there are as many names as there are manufacturers, such as Micrologic, SUHL, MECL, CTL, and UTILOGIC.

Any review of digital integrated circuits must be done in a hurry because the subject matter is so volatile. An example of this was dramatically presented by the entrance of RCA into the arena in the fall of 1965 with the announcement of a fairly complete digital logic group that included ECL (emitter-coupled logic) as well as DTL (diode-transistor logic), along with

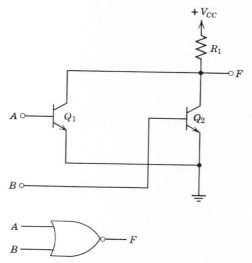

Figure 4.4 DCTL (direct-coupled transistor logic) NOR gate.

linear circuits of video amplifiers, audio amplifiers, differential amplifiers, and operational amplifiers.

Many reviews of digital logic are available, each trying to clarify a rather confusing picture of the capabilities, and lack of them, of the many logic families. This is more difficult than would appear on the surface, because

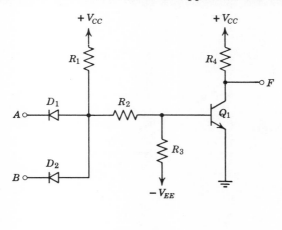

Figure 4.5 DTL (diode-transistor logic) NAND gate.

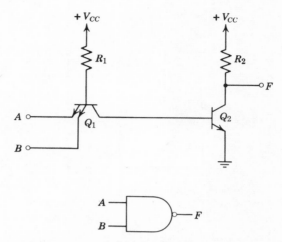

Figure 4.6 T²L (transistor-to-transistor logic) NAND gate.

the design of a "black box" type of equipment is a personal thing, and thus opinions expressed about the capabilities of a black box are also personal. Therefore anyone using IC (integrated circuit) logic develops his own opinions about the logic and, although this is normal and to be expected, it is not always desirable. The IC logic package is a black box. It will have characteristics and features inherent in its own internal circuits and fabrication technique, just as one manufacturer's radio set

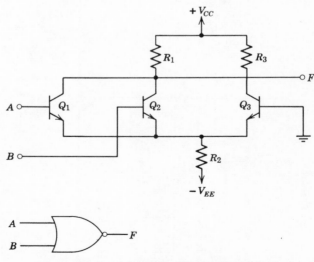

Figure 4.7 CML (current-mode logic) NOR gate.

is different in internal detail from another, even though they both use the same basic functional approach. Thus the speed, power, or fan-out relationships of an integrated monolithic planar diffused logic package leave much to be desired in describing the good and bad features of any individual circuit. Personal experience is by far the best guide, supplemented by detailed reviews by other users.

A review of the characteristics of seven basic logic families is contained in this chapter, with general as well as detailed data for comparative purposes. The data are averages based on published specification sheets and technical articles. The cost of the different logic types is purposely omitted. Not only is the cost picture a fluid one, but the cost of equipment using integrated logic is dependent on the logic family selected for implementation; that is, a 10-bit synchronous counter may require 30 packages at $10.00 per package in one family as opposed to 15 packages at $15 per package in another family, for a cost ratio of $300 : $225. This is obviously not the only factor, since testing, manufacturing, and logistics also play a significant part in the total picture.

The years 1964 and 1965 will probably be recorded as the initial years for microelectronics. The number of manufacturers has fluctuated and will surely continue to do so; however, the basic circuit concepts have definitely begun to stabilize. The emphasis is now shifting toward multifunctional packages such as full adders, decade counters, and BCD converters. Various companies are actively involved in flip-chip and techniques for crossovers. The MOS FET (monolithic oxide-silicon field-effect transistor) shows great promise for use in large multifunctional arrays, because of its simplicity of fabrication and small size.

4.3 BASIC LOGIC FAMILIES

RTL (DCTL)—Fairchild

Fairchild utilized the basic configuration shown in Figure 4.4 to market a compatible set of microelectronic integrated digital logic circuits in 1961. It is called the Fairchild Micrologic family and is manufactured by planar epitaxial diffusion techniques on a monolithic silicon chip. The logic functions are developed from the modified DCTL circuit shown in Figure 4.8, which, because of the addition of the base resistors, has become known as RTL (resistor-transistor logic).

This particular circuit configuration was probably selected by Fairchild because it is simple, cheap to produce, and has good speed-power relationships. The input base resistors were added to prevent current hogging.

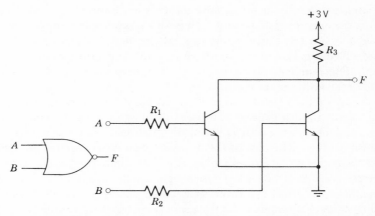

Figure 4.8 RTL (DCTL)—Fairchild. Characteristics: good speed-power product; low fan-out; and low noise immunity.

Micrologic	Milliwatt Micrologic
$R_1 = 450$	$R_1 = 1500$
$R_2 = 450$	$R_2 = 1500$
$R_3 = 640$	$R_3 = 3600$

The magnitude of these base resistors as well as the collector pull-up resistor is not critical and can be varied to produce a wide range of speed-power relationships. The original Micrologic line utilizes a 450-Ω base resistor with a 640-Ω collector resistor for a propagation delay of 12 nsec and a power of 12 mW.

Fairchild later introduced the Milliwatt Micrologic family, which uses a 1500-Ω base resistor with a 3600-Ω collector resistor to achieve an average delay of 40 nsec with an average power of only 4 mW. The Milliwatt line competes with Texas Instruments' Series 51, which is a low-power line.

The success of this logic family was originally due to its availability, simplicity, and, after the price reductions, its low cost. The Micrologic line is still very popular and is second-sourced by Philco, Motorola, Texas Instruments, and others.

RCTL—Texas Instruments

Texas Instruments introduced their Series SN51 modified DCTL circuit in 1961 and called it an RCTL (resistor-capacitor-transistor logic) circuit. This circuit is shown in Figure 4.9 and illustrates the approach Texas Instrument used to achieve a compromise between resistor values and speed and power relationships. Apparently it was felt that power was more significant than speed; thus the large base resistor, which had to be compensated by a capacitor. This circuit was also an attempt to produce a configuration that would "look familiar" to the user in order to be accepted. This intuition was correct; however, it did not go far enough, as was later proven by Signetics.

The significant features of the SN51 series are a low power of 2 mW per gate coupled with a simple configuration that lends itself to low-cost techniques. The basic disadvantage is the slow speed, which prohibits its use in systems with a clock frequency much above 500 kc.

It should be noted that Fairchild chose to make a simple circuit package in the familiar TO-5 can (with eight leads) whereas Texas Instruments sacrificed speed for power and produced a revolutionary 10-lead flat pack that no one knew how to handle. This did not appear significant in the early 1960s, because the space industry was the only one that could afford to pay $50 for a single logic gate in some "absurd" package. However, in the summer of 1964, when Fairchild upset the whole industry by introducing low-temperature RTL commercial-quality integrated circuit packages at a cost of $2.55 to $6.35 in quantities over 100, the entire industry took another look at the cost picture to see just exactly how much it was costing to produce logic circuits.

The SN51 series is characterized by a generous selection of NOR gates and R-S flip-flops as well as separate single shots, clock drivers, and pulsed exclusive-OR. An SN51R high-reliability version is also available.

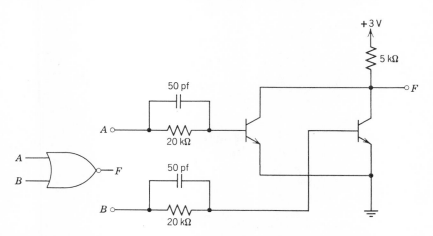

Figure 4.9 Texas Instruments' Series SN51. Characteristics: very low power, but slow; fair noise immunity; and average fan-out.

DTL—Signetics

A relatively new company called Signetics introduced a line of monolithic integrated circuits in the early 1960s using the familiar diode-transistor logic circuit configuration shown in Figure 4.10. This looks exactly like the discrete DTL circuits that the logic designers had been working with, except for the substitution of the two series diodes D_3 and D_4 in the base leg for the cheaper resistor shown in Figure 4.5. If the designer of discrete circuits had had his choice, he too would have preferred the diodes because of their ease of design, predictable operation, and increased speed. In other words, the diodes are an obvious asset and result in lower costs when built into integrated circuits. Signetic elected to package their circuits in a 10-lead TO-5 can, probably because of its familiar shape, but more so because it was a proven, reliable package that cost less than the flat pack.

Signetics—a new company—went up against the formidable giants, Texas Instruments and Fairchild, and momentarily won. The disadvantages of the dual power supplies and the large resistors (and thus large chips) were offset by the familiarity of the circuit design, large voltage swing, and high noise immunity, and this was the most sought-after IC during 1962 and 1963.

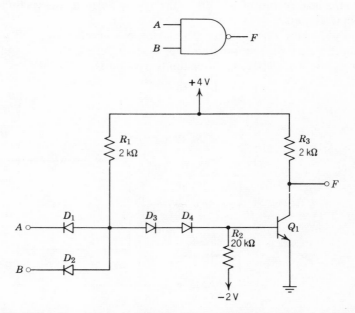

Figure 4.10 DTL—Signetics' Series SE100. Characteristics: good speed at low power; high noise immunity; and average fan-out.

The input diodes increase the input impedance and assist the speed-power relationship. The large pull-up resistor is a disadvantage for fan-out and frequency response but provides a collector OR'ing capability and a large logic level voltage swing, which is desirable for high noise immunities. The logic line is easy to program with and understand, because of its familiar circuit. It has a good speed-power product level but is somewhat limited in fan-out. The basic logic gates bring out the pull-up resistor so that it may be omitted when collectors are being wired together or when reduced power is desired. Loading rules are somewhat confusing, but there is a learning curve associated with any of the logic families. Logic selection is fairly good, with a broad selection of NAND gates and power drivers.

DTL (Modified)—Texas Instruments

In the latter part of 1963 Texas Instruments introduced a modified diode transistor logic with the SN53 series shown in Figure 4.11. The object of this family is to enhance the basic logic concept of the DTL circuit by making full utilization of IC techniques. This was accomplished through two significant changes: p-n-p input transistors instead of just diodes, and a totem-pole or push-pull output stage.

This configuration was one of the first to take full advantage of the monolithic structure relative to the theme "transistors are cheap; resistors and

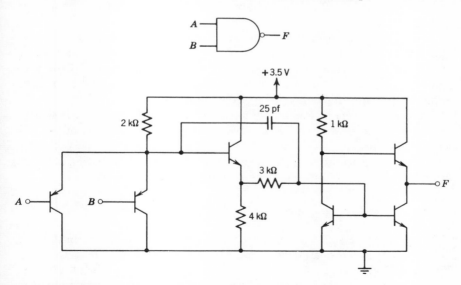

Figure 4.11 DTL (modified)—Texas Instruments' Series 53. Characteristics: reasonable speed-power relationships; high fan-out; and good noise immunity.

capacitors are expensive." The monolithic integrated triple-diffused structure provides the p-n-p input transistors without significant change from the p-n diode inputs simply by terminating the p substrate. This provides the input points with a stage that has gain. The 2-kΩ resistor to B+ on the input of the DTL gates has to have reasonably good tolerance control. It should be small in order to switch the output transistor, but large in order not to reduce fan-outs. The use of a transistor in place of the diode significantly reduces the tolerance requirements on this resistor. Furthermore, replacement of the dual-level dropping diodes D_3 and D_4 with an emitter-follower also diminishes the significance of this resistor. However, inclusion of this emitter-follower adds power dissipation, since a couple of resistors must be included to control voltage levels, as well as a capacitor to speed up turn-off of this emitter-follower.

The final unique characteristic of this circuit is its push-pull output configuration. The design is such that only one transistor is on at a time, providing a power current driver or a power current sink. This results in well-defined logic levels for both the 1 and 0 states (instead of depending on a pull-up resistor) and provides a low-impedance source of about 50 Ω for both logic levels. This low-impedance push-pull output not only is significant for its increased fan-out capability at high speed, but also provides a significant improvement in a-c noise immunity. Noise pick-up on a line terminated in a low impedance of 50 Ω is obviously going to be less than a line terminated in a 2-kΩ impedance. This is a significant factor in large logic systems.

It should be noted that this was the first logic series to introduce a *J-K* flip-flop. This is again the result of free use of active elements to produce many gates on a single chip. The *J-K* flip-flop is important in logic programming, as its use can result in a significant reduction of total logic gates required for implementation of a given function.

The loading rules of this family are simple, and it is easy to utilize with a large fan-out of 10. The series provides a generous selection of NAND gates, including a quad-2 input gate package as well as a dual exclusive-OR pack. The selection of flip-flops includes a positive and negative logic programming capability along with two flip-flops in a package.

DTL (Improved)—Fairchild

What might be called an improved diode-transistor logic was introduced by Fairchild in 1964, as their DTμL series. The basic circuit is shown in Figure 4.12 and reflects a "familiar" logic circuit with significant advances over Signetics' original design, shown in Figure 4.10. These significant advances are in the speed-power relationships and result from the addition of a split collector-resistor (R_1 and R_2) to an otherwise conventional integrated logic circuit. The intermediate-gain stage, Q_1, allows wide resistor tolerances, provides strong base drive to the output stage, increasing fan-out ability, and allows use of a small pull-down resistor, R_3, to eliminate the need for a negative power supply. The design of the resistor-divider is such that the intermediate-gain transistor, Q_1, does not go into saturation, thereby increasing speed and minimizing the transient current on the input line during switching.

This circuit reflects the optimization of a conventional logic "schematic" with monolithic integrated circuit techniques. Its features are its reasonably high speed with low power for an excellent speed-power relationships. The configuration is simple to comprehend, and thus the learning curve associated with its utilization should be a short one. The logic selection, although small, is adequate, providing a quad-2 input NAND gate, a dual-4 input gate with expander connections, and a *J-K* flip-flop. Fan-out is a reasonable 8, and noise immunity is very good. Collector OR'ing can be done, improving the versatility.

One disadvantage inherent in this type of logic circuit is the large pull-up

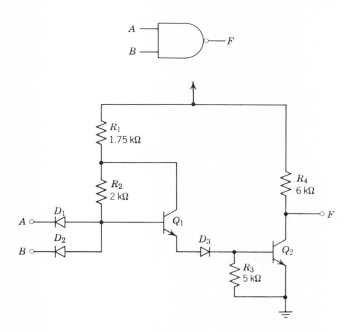

Figure 4.12 DTL (improved)—Fairchild DTμL series. Characteristics: good speed with low power; good fan-out; and good noise immunity.

resistor, R_4. Although it reduces power, it also provides a high-impedance source for ac noise pickup.

This family is second-sourced by Philco, Texas Instruments, and others.

ECL—Motorola

In 1961 General Electric announced a family of integrated logic circuits called emitter-coupled logic operators (ECLO) based on the circuit of Figure 4.7. However, the application and logic rules they published along with the circuits were intended for the circuit designer and tended to confuse the logic designer. Such statements as " permissible fan-out is h_{FE} divided by 3 " did not go over very well.

Motorola used the same circuit concept with a different approach. They evolved a very-high-speed logic family, called Motorola emitter-coupled logic (MECL), based on the approach shown in Figure 4.13. This circuit configuration takes advantage of the fastest mode of operation of a transistor —a common base mode—along with nonsaturated logic to achieve delay times well under 10 nsec. In the era of demands for higher-speed computers this Motorola circuit was desperately needed. It provided unheard-of speeds of 20-mHz capability, extremely high fan-out of 25, and the unusual features of a NOR and an OR output. These advantages are paid

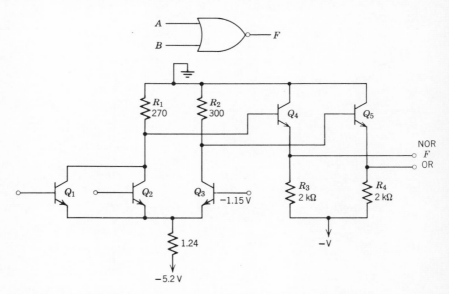

Figure 4.13 ECL (MECL)—Motorola emitter-coupled logic. Characteristics: very high speed; low noise immunity; and very high fan-out.

for with a low noise margin, a secondary power supply or inclusion of a bias driver, and increased power.

The bias driver circuit was a clever answer to providing not only the secondary power supply required to establish the bias level for the current mode gate, but also a source for temperature compensation as well when it is mounted adjacent to the other logic gates.

The NOR-OR outputs are easy to come by with integrated techniques, and tend to balance power dissipation and power supply loading while improving the versatility of the logic family. Direct-current input impedance of an emitter-follower, common-base configuration is inherently high, providing large fan-in as well as fan-out capability. This circuit configuration has been used to develop logic circuits with propagation delays under 1 nsec.

The MECL series has been broadened to provide a versatile logic family. The *J-K* flip-flop, although slow to be provided, enhances the flexibility along with the quad-2 input NOR gate. Outputs can be wired together to perform logic functions at a reduced gate requirement. Fan-out is excel- and increased fan-in is easy to come by.

The low logic level swing and its negative levels usually require interface circuitry into and out of the MECL series, and also result in poor noise immunity. However, if speed is significant, design considerations can minimize these weaknesses.

T^2L—Sylvania

Monolithic planar diffused techniques lend themselves to a logic circuit not readily adaptable to discrete components, in the form of transistor-to-transistor logic (T^2L) shown in Figure 4.6. This multiple emitter configuration is a natural in diffused integrated circuits, as well as providing speed advantages over the conventional DTL diode inputs.

Sylvania was one of the first companies to take advantage of this concept, with a family of logic circuits introduced in 1963 based on the circuit shown in Figure 4.14. The turn-on time of output transistor Q_1 in the DTL gate of Figure 4.10 is limited by the recovery time of input diodes D_1 and D_2. The T^2L circuit replaces these input diodes, along with the level-shifting diodes D_3 and D_4, with a multiple emitter transistor configuration that performs the same function with inherently much higher speed capability. An active transistor pull-up network in the output allows rapid charging or discharging of capacitance loads as high as 600 pf. The output is at a low impedance in either the ON or the OFF state, which greatly minimizes the pick-up of noise. Short-circuit protection is built into the circuit as a result of series resistor R_4 in the pull-up network.

This was the first logic line to combine very high speed with high logic level

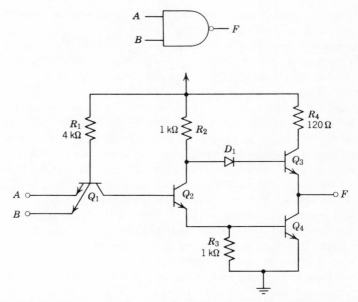

Figure 4.14 T²L—Sylvania SUHL I. Characteristics: high speed with low power; high noise immunity; and high fan-out.

swings. However, the relatively high cost of these circuits from Sylvania kept them reserved for special situations. This condition has been remedied, and the use of T²L logic is rapidly increasing.

The introduction in 1964 by Sylvania of the first T²L *J-K* flip-flop did much to enhance the line's flexibility, but originally there was no need to pay the high price of these circuits unless requirements for speed and noise immunity precluded the use of any other circuit. The line, when first available, introduced an almost confusing array of NAND gates, exclusive-OR gates, and various combinations of multifunction circuits. This has since been tempered with a more sober assortment that includes quad-2 input with expander and the most versatile *J-K* flip-flops in the industry.

Sylvania also has a Sylvania Universal High-Level Logic (SUHL II) line, which has propagation delays of 6 nsec and power dissipation of 22 mW. This represents one of the lowest speed-power products in the industry.

The T²L configuration is also being produced by Texas Instruments as their Series SN54. The circuits are basically identical, except that Texas Instruments has taken diode D_1 and placed it between the emitter Q_3 and the output mode. The Texas Instruments family is more conservative in the variety of logic configurations provided.

Table 4.5 is a generalized comparison of the fundamental logic types.

TABLE 4.5 Relative Characteristics

Logic family	Type	Propagation delay (nsec)	Power dissipation (mW)	Speed-power	Fan-out	Noise immunity (mV)
Fairchild μL	RTL	B	B	B	D	D
Fairchild MWμL	RTL	C	A	B	D	D
TI SN51	RCTL	D	A	C	C	D
Signetics SE100	DTL	C	A	B	C	B
TI SN53 DTL		C	B	C	B	C
Fairchild DTμL	DTL	B	A	B	B	B
Sylvania SUHL I	T²L	B	B	B	B	B
TI SN54	T²L	B	B	B	B	B
Sylvania SUHL II	T²L	A	B	B	B	B
Motorola MECL	ECL	A	B	B	A	D
Signetics SE180	DTL	B	B	C	B	C
Signetics SE480	T²L	C	A	C	C	C
Coded weights	A	<10	<10	<100	>10	>1000
	B	10–25	10–25	100–250	8–10	501–1000
	C	26–100	26–100	251–500	5–7	300–500
	D	>100	>100	>500	<5	<300

4.4 ADDITIONAL LOGIC OUTGROWTHS

Signetics—UTILOGIC

The Signetics UTILOGIC series is a logic form developed for application in commercial, industrial, and ground-support equipment. The family includes a T²L AND gate, an emitter-follower input with a push-pull–powered output NOR gate, and a diode input-powered output *J-K* flip-flop. The line has limiting fan-out rules but is essentially easy to work with. The logic swing is 0.6 to $+3.3$ V for the NOR gate and thus has good noise immunity.

Signetics—Monolithic DTL Elements

Signetics has introduced an improved DTL configuration characterized by their SE180 NAND gate, shown in Figure 4.15. This circuit replaces the voltage-dropping diodes with an emitter-follower Q_1 (much as Fairchild did) in order to improve the tolerance restrictions on the resistors, eliminate

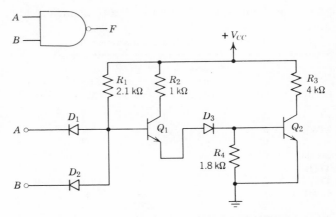

Figure 4.15 DTL (improved)—Signetics SE180.

the need for a pull-down voltage supply, and increase the fan-out characteristics. This series includes a variety of NAND gates, an *R-S* flip-flop, *J-K* flip-flop, and a monostable multivibrator. It is compatible with their SE100 series.

Fairchild—CTL

Fairchild announced a family called complementary transistor micrologic (CTμL) in March 1965. It was designed for very-high-speed, low-cost commercial applications. Average propagation delays of 5 nsec per gate can be achieved through the use of the AND-OR-NOR logic design techniques. Noise margins are typically 0.5 V, with an associated logic swing of 3 V. Power dissipation is a function of fan-out and fan-in as a result of the emitter-follower output stages and resistor-buffered p-n-p input stages.

The complementary transistor connotation derives from the use of p-n-p transistors as inputs to the logic gates and n-p-n transistors for the rest of the networks. The basic configuration of the AND gate does not provide inversion—just current gain by use of an emitter-follower output. This also requires a negative pull-down power supply. All the circuits have provision for OR ties.

These circuits are packaged in the larger 14-lead commercial package with output pins on 0.1-in. centers.

Motorola—VTL

Motorola introduced a variable-threshold logic (VTL) in August 1965, which can be adjusted to provide noise immunities from 2 to 5 V as a function of the $+V_{CC}$ and $-V_{EE}$. The family is essentially a modified form of DTL logic as shown in Figure 4.16.

The circuit differs from the conventional diode transistor logic by using emitter-follower Q_1 and resistor R_2 to replace the voltage-dropping diodes. The pull-down resistor is replaced by a constant current source, Q_3. The amount of current depends on the supply levels and the ratio R_4/R_6. Q_3 provides a current through offset resistor R_2. The voltage across R_2 determines the input threshold of the circuit. The input threshold is altered by changing the bias on Q_3, which changes the current through R_2. The larger the current through R_2, the larger the voltage drop across R_2 and thus the larger the input threshold level. In order to maintain similar noise immunities for high- and low-level logic the V_{CC} and V_{EE} supplies are made equal, and both are varied to change noise immunity.

Circuit speed, power dissipation, and noise immunity are all interrelated. An increase in power-supply voltage increases the power dissipated in the circuit, but provides faster operating speeds. Typical propagation delay of the VTL gate will vary from 60 nsec with 4-V supplies to 48 nsec with 10-V supplies at 25°C.

These circuits are currently specified for operation over a 0°C to +70°C temperature range.

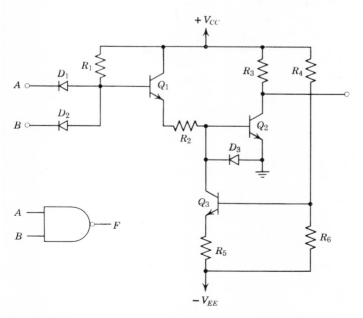

Figure 4.16 VTL—Motorola variable-threshold logic.

4.5 COMMENTS

As of this writing there are more than 25 manufacturers of digital integrated circuits. The previous discussion is not intended to slight or highlight any particular manufacturer except as a result of their contribution to the development of ICs and/or the popularity of their particular logic family. Cross-licensing between manufacturers has provided second sources for all the high-volume circuits. This practice has developed to the point where certain popular analog circuits are available from multiple sources.

As the circuit types have narrowed down to the basic high-volume DTL, TTL, and ECL configurations the manufacturers have begun to exploit multifunctional circuits in a single package. Complete decade counters are available in a single package; 8-bit shift registers, 4-bit counters, 4 × 4 memory cells, full adders, dual flip-flops, complete BCD decoders, diode matrices, D/A converters, multiswitch elements, and many others can be had. The next step in bipolar design would appear to be LSI (large-scale integration), whereby a complete computing functional unit is made from one monolithic wafer.

Another area that has yet to receive its full credit is that of MOS FETS (metal oxide-silicon field-effect transistor). Progress in the application of MOS FETS has been slow as a result of problems related to temperature stability and frequency of application. However, these devices still show the greatest potential promise of all the multifunctional computing units in a given area, because of their small geometry and fewer processing steps. The 100-bit shift register in a TO-5 can is the most vivid example of the potentials of the MOS FET technology.

5

COMBINATIONAL LOGIC

Logic design has to do with the analysis, synthesis, minimization, and implementation of binary functions. Boolean algebra provides the analytical techniques to analyze and minimize binary functions, but now comes the questions: "Where does the Boolean function come from?" and "How is the Boolean function used?" These questions can be restated to read: "How does one synthesize a binary requirement?" and "How does one implement a Boolean equation?"

Synthesis can be defined as the conversion of a statement or problem into a Boolean algebraic expression. This brings to mind the classic problem associated with high-school algebra, that of trying to create the algebraic expression from the stated words. The difficulty of this type of problem has not been eased. The written or spoken word is full of misinterpretations.

For example, suppose the instructions were to synthesize a logic function that would provide an output if input A was present or if input B was present. This is represented in Figure 5.1. A logic function to fulfill this requirement is given by $f = A + B$. A block diagram, the equation, and analysis are shown in Figure 5.1.

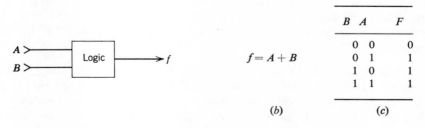

B	A	F
0	0	0
0	1	1
1	0	1
1	1	1

(b)   (c)

Figure 5.1 (a) Block diagram; (b) function; (c) analysis.

An analysis of this equation shows that the function is true if A is present, if B is present, or if both A and B are present. This final phrase, that the function is true if A and B are present, may not be desired. However, there was nothing stated about this condition in the problem and therefore the above function satisfies the stated problem.

However, the function $f = A\bar{B} + \bar{A}B$ also satisfies the stated problem in the literal sense. Analysis of this function is shown in Figure 5.2. Here the function is not true when both A and B are true but is true if A or B is true. This function is referred to as the exclusive-OR whereas the previous equation is the inclusive-OR. This is a subtle but very significant distinction.

	B	A	f
	0	0	0
$f - A\bar{B} + \bar{A}B$	0	1	1
	1	0	1
	1	1	0

(a)   (b)

Figure 5.2 (a) Function; (b) analysis.

The point is that the originator of the stated problem may not be a logic designer. He is simply stating a need. The logic designer must account for all possible combinations of conditions in synthesizing a requirement. Once an equation is written it automatically accounts for all possible combinations of the variables. It is then up to the analysis to verify that the synthesis does in fact fulfill the requirements. Furthermore, it is the responsibility of the logic designer to review the synthesis and analysis with the originator of the requirements to be sure the solution is suitable.

5.1 ANALYSIS

Combinational logic refers to networks whose output is strictly dependent on its inputs. The analysis of such networks requires first the writing of the Boolean algebraic equation representative of the network, and then the complete characterization of the output as a result of all the possible combinations of the inputs.

EXAMPLE 5.1. The network shown in Figure 5.3 is dependent on the variables A, B, C, and D. This indicates that the output is a function of all four of the inputs. In order to determine just what particular combination of inputs will provide an output, an analysis of the function must be performed. An inspection of the network indicates that the three variables A,

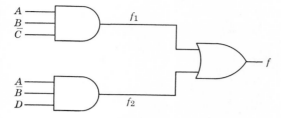

Figure 5.3.

B, and $\bar{C}$ are AND'ed in one gate and that the variables A, $\bar{B}$, and D are AND'ed in another gate. The output of these two AND gates is OR'ed to provide the final output. Thus

$$f_1 = AB\bar{C}$$
$$f_2 = A\bar{B}D$$
$$f = f_1 + f_2$$
$$f = AB\bar{C} + A\bar{B}D.$$

This final function is analyzed in a Karnaugh map and a truth table in Figure 5.4. The map and the truth table completely define the function. The result is that the output is 1 when A is 1 AND B is 1 AND C is 0 OR when A is 1 AND B is 0 AND D is 1. For any other combination of inputs the

$f = AB\bar{C} + A\bar{B}D$

(a)

No.	D	C	B	A	f
0	0	0	0	0	0
1	0	0	0	1	0
2	0	0	1	0	0
3	0	0	1	1	1
4	0	1	0	0	0
5	0	1	0	1	0
6	0	1	1	0	0
7	0	1	1	1	0
8	1	0	0	0	0
9	1	0	0	1	1
10	1	0	1	0	0
11	1	0	1	1	1
12	1	1	0	0	0
13	1	1	0	1	1
14	1	1	1	0	0
15	1	1	1	1	0

$C \backslash A$ $D \backslash$ B	00	01	11	10
00	0	0	1	0
01	0	0	1	1
11	0	0	0	1
10	0	0	0	0

(b)

(c)

Figure 5.4 (a) Function; (b) map; (c) truth table.

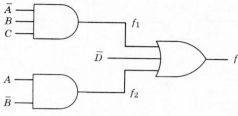

Figure 5.5.

output is 0. In talking about this network it may sometimes be more convenient to state that the output is 1 for the numbers 3, 9, 11, and 13; otherwise it is 0. The map or the truth table clearly, concisely, and unambiguously defines the output as a function of all the possible combinations of the inputs.

EXAMPLE 5.2. Another example is the analysis of the network in Figure 5.5. The first step is to write the algebraic expression for the network. The network consists of one 3-input AND gate, one 2-input AND gate, and one 3-input OR gate. The outputs of the two AND gates are OR'ed together to form the final output. Thus

$$f_1 = \bar{A}BC$$
$$f_2 = A\bar{B}$$
$$f = f_1 + \bar{D} + f_2$$
$$= \bar{A}BC + \bar{D} + A\bar{B}.$$

$$f = \bar{A}BC + \bar{D} + A\bar{B}$$

(a)

C A				
D B	00	01	11	10
00	1	1	1	1
01	0	0	0	1
11	0	1	0	1
10	1	1	1	1

(b)

No.	D	C	B	A	f
0	0	0	0	0	1
1	0	0	0	1	1
2	0	0	1	0	1
3	0	0	1	1	1
4	0	1	0	0	1
5	0	1	0	1	1
6	0	1	1	0	1
7	0	1	1	1	1
8	1	0	0	0	0
9	1	0	0	1	1
10	1	0	1	0	0
11	1	0	1	1	0
12	1	1	0	0	0
13	1	1	0	1	1
14	1	1	1	0	1
15	1	1	1	1	0

(c)

Figure 5.6 (a) Function; (b) map; (c) truth table.

This function is defined by the truth table and map in Figure 5.6, from which it can be seen the output is 1 for the numerical combinations 0, 1, 2, 3, 4, 5, 6, 7, 9, 13, and 14. It might be easier to say that the output is 1 for all inputs except 8, 10, 11, 12, and 15. Obviously the map is a more condensed version, but the truth table has pictorial appeal. Some more examples of analysis follow.

EXAMPLE 5.3. Figure 5.7 illustrates the AND'ing of three OR gates to form a network. This results in a product of sums expression that is mapped either by mapping the zero terms, as shown, or by multiplying the terms together to get a sum of products form. Any technique that results in a correct analysis is valid. Experience and/or training usually determines the approach used by the designer. Notice in this example that minimization techniques can be applied to the analysis to reduce the implementation. That is, writing a minimal expression from the map will require only three 2-input OR gates instead of the one 3-input and two 2-input OR gates. This is shown in Figure 5.8. Also shown are two other expressions that can be used to implement the function. Possibly the last expression, requiring one 3-input AND gate and one 2-input AND gate OR'ed together, would be

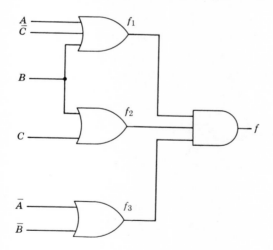

$$f_1 = A + \bar{C} + B$$

$$f_2 = B + C$$

$$f_3 = \bar{A} + \bar{B}$$

$$f = f_1 \cdot f_2 \cdot f_3$$

$$= (A + B + \bar{C})(B + C)(\bar{A} + \bar{B})$$

(b)

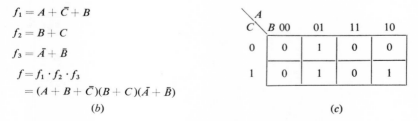

(c)

Figure 5.7 (a) Network; (b) equations; (c) map.

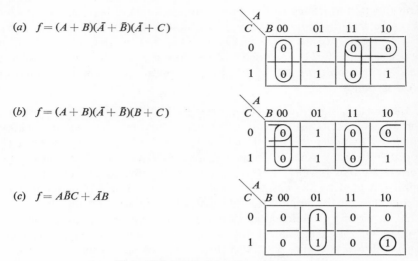

(a) $f = (A + B)(\bar{A} + \bar{B})(\bar{A} + C)$

(b) $f = (A + B)(\bar{A} + \bar{B})(B + C)$

(c) $f = A\bar{B}C + \bar{A}B$

Figure 5.8 Minimizing Example 5.3.

more desirable. At any rate, the analysis not only shows all the possible combinational states but provides the means for minimizing the function and obtaining other possible expressions just as valid.

EXAMPLE 5.4. One way of approaching the problem in Figure 5.9 is to assign numbers to the output of each gate, then, slowly and systematically,

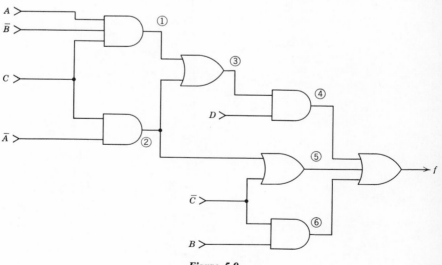

Figure 5.9.

starting at the output, work back toward the input until all numbers have been replaced by the inputs.

$$f = ④ + ⑤ + ⑥$$
$$④ = D \cdot ③$$
$$⑤ = \bar{C} + ②$$
$$⑥ = B \cdot \bar{C}$$
$$③ = ① + ②$$
$$② = \bar{A} \cdot C$$
$$① = A \cdot \bar{B} \cdot C,$$

giving $f = ④ + ⑤ + ⑥$
$$= D \cdot ③ + \bar{C} + ② + B \cdot \bar{C}$$
$$= D(\cdot ① + ②) + \bar{D} + \bar{A}C + B\bar{C}$$
$$= D(A\bar{B}C + \bar{A}C) + \bar{C} + \bar{A}C + B\bar{C}.$$

Obviously some minimization can be performed on this function. Thus the next step is to analyze the expression

$\begin{smallmatrix}C&\diagdown&A\\D&\diagdown&B\end{smallmatrix}$ 00	01	11	10
00 1	1	1	1
01 1	1	1	1
11 1	1	0	1
10 1	1	0	0

$$= A\bar{B}CD + \bar{A}CD + \bar{C} + \bar{A}C + B\bar{C}.$$

The analysis of the function by the map indicates that considerable reduction can be made. A minimal function can be quickly written by grouping the 0's.

$\begin{smallmatrix}C&\diagdown&A\\D&\diagdown&B\end{smallmatrix}$ 00	01	11	10
00 1	1	1	1
01 1	1	1	1
11 1	1	0	1
10 1	1	0	0

$$f = (\bar{A} + \bar{B} + \bar{C})(\bar{A} + \bar{C} + D)$$
also $f = \bar{A} + \bar{C} + \bar{B}D.$

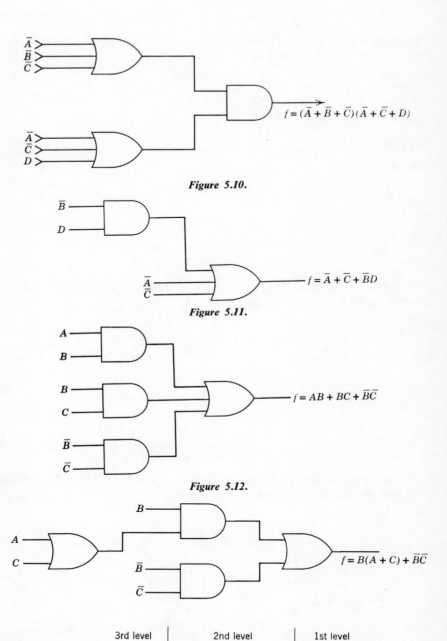

$$f = (\overline{A} + \overline{B} + \overline{C})(\overline{A} + \overline{C} + D)$$

Figure 5.10.

$$f = \overline{A} + \overline{C} + \overline{B}D$$

Figure 5.11.

$$f = AB + BC + \overline{B}\overline{C}$$

Figure 5.12.

$$f = B(A + C) + \overline{B}\overline{C}$$

| 3rd level | 2nd level | 1st level |

Figure 5.13.

94

Implementation of the first function can be accomplished by two 3-input OR gates and one AND gate (Fig. 5.10). It can also be implemented with one 2-input AND gate and a 3-input OR gate (Fig. 5.11). This latter implementation apparently results in fewer logic gates and may be the most desirable.

The analysis and implementation of AND and OR logic are relatively simple and straightforward. The sum of terms requires an OR gate whereas the product of terms requires an AND gate. A standard form implies a second-order implementation whereas factored forms require third-order or higher. That is, the function $f = AB + BC + \overline{B}\overline{C}$ is a second-order equation and requires only two levels of logic: three 2-input AND gates with an output OR gate (Fig. 5.12). A factored form of this function, $f = B(A + C) + \overline{B}\overline{C}$, requires an output OR gate, two 2-input AND gates, with one of the AND gates preceded by an OR gate (Fig. 5.13). A four-level logic function would be represented by $f = B(A + CD) + \overline{B}\overline{C}$ (Fig. 5.14).

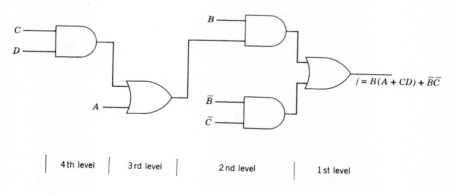

Figure 5.14.

5.2 NAND-NOR LOGIC ANALYSIS

The analysis of logic functions implemented with NAND gates or NOR gates need not be any more difficult than if it were composed of AND or OR gates. Maley and Earle (see bibliography) state that a series connection of an even number of NAND gates has the appearance of an AND gate whereas a series connection of an odd number of NAND gates has the appearance of an OR gate.

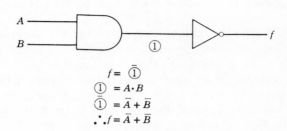

$$f = \overline{①}$$
$$① = A \cdot B$$
$$\overline{①} = \bar{A} + \bar{B}$$
$$\therefore f = \bar{A} + \bar{B}$$

Figure 5.15

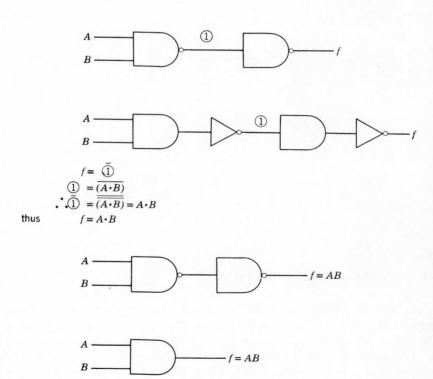

$$f = \overline{①}$$
$$① = \overline{(A \cdot B)}$$
$$\therefore \overline{①} = \overline{\overline{(A \cdot B)}} = A \cdot B$$

thus $f = A \cdot B$

Figure 5.16.

NAND Logic

A NAND gate can be considered as an AND gate with an inverter on its output. A circle at the output of a gate signifies an inverter. Thus a NAND gate by itself (an odd-level gate) has the appearance of an OR gate with the inputs inverted. This is evident from an examination of the function shown in Figure 5.15. A series connection of two NAND gates (an even number) has the appearance of an AND gate (Fig. 5.16).

A series connection of NAND gates can be identified as a series connection of AND and OR gates by assigning all "even"-level gates as AND and all "odd"-level gates as OR, starting with the output gate.

Some examples will illustrate the approach.

EXAMPLE 5.5

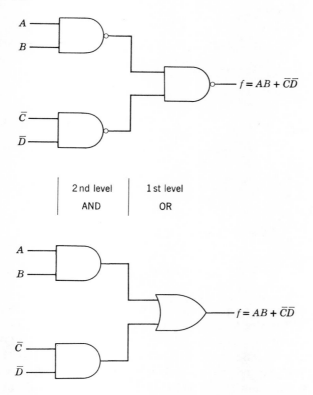

In Example 5.5, tracing the variable A through from the input to the output carries it through two inverters, one for each NAND gate. It is reasonable, therefore, to expect that because A is complemented twice the output should contain A in the same form as it entered. This is equivalent to

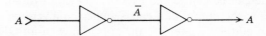

The state of any input, whether it should be complemented or not, thus depends on whether it passes through an even number of inverters or an odd number of inverters. If the variable passes through an even number of inverters it should appear in the output in the same form as it entered. If it passes through an odd number of inverters it should appear at the output as the complement.

EXAMPLE 5.6

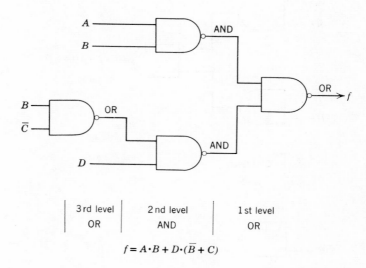

$$f = A \cdot B + D \cdot (\bar{B} + C)$$

Example 5.6 illustrates a three-level logic implementation. Starting with the output, the odd or first logic level NAND gate has the effect of an OR gate. The second or even level has the appearance of an AND gate. The third level, which is odd, must be treated as an OR gate. This is equivalent to picturing the implementation as shown in Figure 5.17. Once the function is written in this manner, however, an examination is made to determine those variables that enter at an odd level. These variables must be complemented at the output. Thus B appears as $\bar{B}$ whereas $\bar{C}$ appears as C in the output.

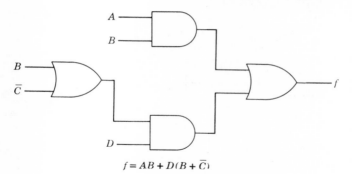

$$f = AB + D(B + \overline{C})$$

Figure 5.17.

A generalized set of rules can now be established when dealing with NAND gates:

1. Identify all NAND gates at odd levels as OR gates.
2. Identify all NAND gates at even levels as AND gates.
3. Invert all variables that enter the logic group at an odd level.

This set of rules implies that in a series string of NAND gates, the gates, starting at the output, alternate as OR-AND-OR-AND ... logic gates. This is illustrated in Figure 5.18. The variables C and E enter at odd levels; therefore they are complemented in the output.

Quite often a variable or a gate serves as an input to more than one gate. In this case a single gate may have to be treated as an AND gate through one path and an OR gate through another path. Example 5.7 is just such a case. The variable A is an input to both an odd level and an even level. This should not cause any confusion, however, if the two separate inputs are treated as if they were separate variables. Once the expression is written, analysis and minimization techniques can be applied to analyze and/or minimize.

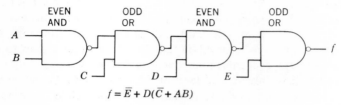

$$f = \overline{E} + D(\overline{C} + AB)$$

Figure 5.18.

EXAMPLE 5.7.

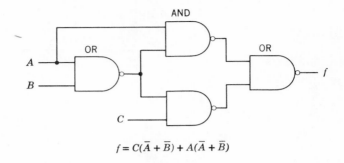

$$f = C(\bar{A} + \bar{B}) + A(\bar{A} + \bar{B})$$

EXAMPLE 5.8.

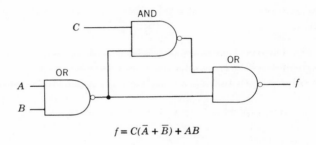

$$f = C(\bar{A} + \bar{B}) + AB$$

Example 5.8 illustrates a single gate occupying a dual role. As an input to the upper gate it is treated as an odd-level or OR gate, whereas its input through the lower path is at an even level. Thus a gate must be treated as a function of the path to the output and the counting is always done from the output to the input. The inputs to this gate, A and B, must also be treated accordingly. That is, the variables A and B pass through an odd number of gates through the upper path and must be complemented at the output. However, they pass through an even number of gates in the lower path, and so they are not complemented in the AND term.

EXAMPLE 5.9. $f = \bar{B}(\bar{E} + \dot{F}) + \bar{D} + \bar{E}(\bar{A} + B)[\bar{D} + (\bar{A} + \bar{B})(A + \bar{C}) + \bar{A}C]$.

In Example 5.9 the gates have been numbered to assist in the explanation. The output gate, ①, is an odd-level gate and is an OR function. Gate ② is an even-level gate and is an AND function. The same applies to gate ④. Gate ⑥ is an ODD-level gate; thus it acts as an OR. Gate ③ only goes into gate ②, and so it is only an odd-level or OR gate. Gate ⑤ only enters gate ③, and so it is an even-level and thus an AND gate. Gate ⑦, in its path to the output, goes via ⑤, ③, ②, and ①, acting as an OR gate, but it also goes

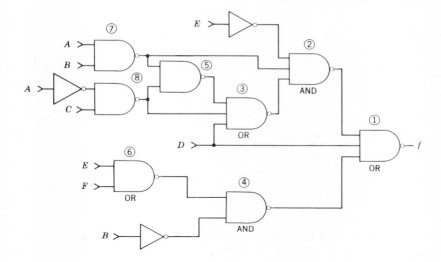

via ② and ①; because this is an odd-level count as well, however, it still acts as an OR gate. However, gate ⑧ passes through ③, ②, and ① in one path to act as an AND gate and through ⑤, ③, ②, and ① to act as an OR gate. All inputs to OR gates are odd-level inputs and must be inverted at the output. All inputs to AND gates are even-level inputs and remain unchanged at the output.

An aid to analyzing any problem of this complexity is to break it into major blocks. Output gate ① has three inputs. Take each input one at a time and draw a separate logic diagram as shown in Figures 5.19 and 5.20. The bottom leg through gates ④ and ⑥ is not too difficult. The middle leg is simply composed of the input D. Thus $f_2 = \bar{D}$. The upper leg is the complex one. An additional break-up of this leg may be helpful in preventing errors as shown in Figure 5.21. Because gate ② is the next complex leg it

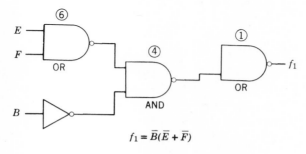

$$f_1 = \bar{B}(\bar{E} + \bar{F})$$

Figure 5.19.

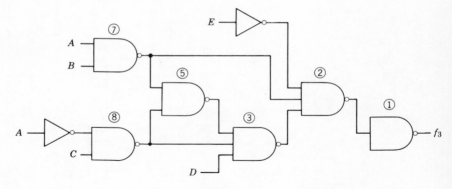

Figure 5.20.

would probably help to diagram each input to gate ② separately, remembering that gate ② has the position and effect of an AND gate. It can be seen that f_3 is the product of f_4, f_5, and f_6 because gate ② is an AND gate. Therefore

$$f_3 = f_4 \cdot f_5 \cdot f_6$$
$$= \bar{E}(\bar{A} + \bar{B})[\bar{D} + (\bar{A} + \bar{B})(A + \bar{C}) + \bar{A}C].$$

The summation of f_1, f_2, and f_3 by gate ① is the total output, and

$$f = f_1 + f_2 + f_3$$
$$= \bar{B}(\bar{E} + \bar{F}) + \bar{D} + \bar{E}(\bar{A} + \bar{B})[\bar{D} + (\bar{A} + \bar{B})(A + \bar{C}) + \bar{A}C].$$

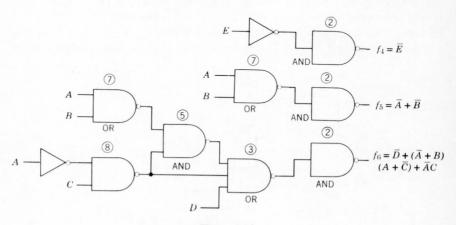

Figure 5.21.

NOR Logic

The analysis of NOR gates is identical with that of NAND gates, except that all odd-level NOR gates act like AND gates and all even-level NOR gates act like OR gates. Example 5.10 illustrates a two-level function:

EXAMPLE 5.10

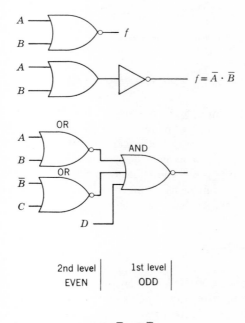

$$f = (A + B)(\bar{B} + C)\bar{D}$$

In Example 5.10 the output NOR gate is an odd-level one; thus it acts as an AND gate. The next two NOR gates are at an even level; thus they act as OR gates. Inputs to equivalent AND gates are at an odd level and must be inverted in the output expression. Thus the output of Example 5.10 is an AND'ing of three terms. One of these terms is $\bar{D}$. Another term is $(A + B)$, and the final term is $(\bar{B} + C)$.

EXAMPLE 5.11

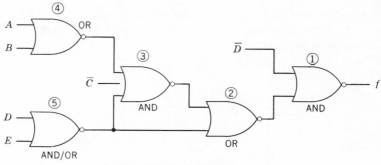

$$f = D \left[\bar{D}E + (D + \bar{E})C(A + B) \right]$$

The output of Example 5.11 consists of D AND'ed with another expression. This expression, made up of D and the output of gate ②, also contains two functions that are OR'ed together. NOR gate ③, at an odd level, acts as an AND gate, just as gate ⑤, as an input to gate ②, is at an odd level. However, gate ⑤ has the effect of an AND gate when viewed as in input to gate ③. Care must be taken to ascertain the path of analysis being followed to obtain the correct function.

5.3 IMPLEMENTATION

This particular section will deal with implementation of the Boolean function. The normal steps in logic design are creating a word statement of the problem or some definitive requirement that is to be satisfied; creation of the algebraic expression representative of the problem; minimization and/or manipulation of the algebraic expression; and, finally, creation of the actual logic diagram that will satisfy these requirements.

Digital integrated circuits have made the job of logic implementation simple. Once the concepts of NAND-NOR logic are understood it should be apparent that a sum of products is simply a two-level NAND gate requirement. The output NAND gate serves to provide the OR function, whereas the second-level NAND gates provide the AND terms.

EXAMPLE 5.12

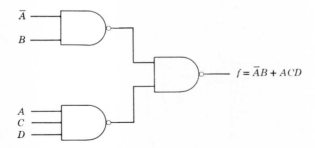

$$f = \overline{A}B + ACD$$

Example 5.12 is a simple OR'ing of two AND terms. The two-level NAND gates provide the logic implementation without requiring inverters or logic manipulation. Thus the standard sum form of equation can be implemented directly by the use of NAND gates. It will result in a two-logic-level implementation and the propagation delay will be that of two NAND gates in series. Examples 5.13, 5.14, and 5.15 are further illustrations of this process.

EXAMPLE 5.13. *Implement* $f = A\overline{C} + B\overline{C}D + ACD$ *with* NAND *gates.*

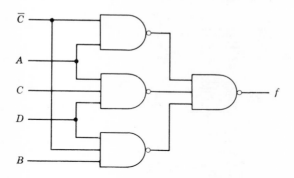

EXAMPLE 5.14. *Implement, with* NAND *gates,* $f = AB + BD + D\overline{C} + \overline{A}\overline{B}$.

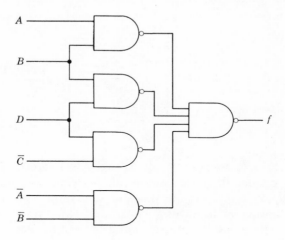

EXAMPLE 5.15. *Implement, with* NAND *gates,* $f = A\overline{B}CDE + \overline{A}B\overline{C}\,\overline{D}E + A\overline{B}\overline{C}$.

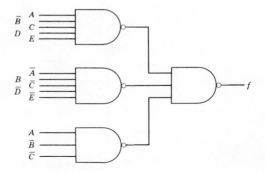

These examples are straightforward. The first-level NAND gate is an OR gate, whereas the second-level gate acts as an AND gate. Thus the equation is implemented exactly as it is written. Because the inputs are entering the logic on an even-level or AND gate, the inputs will not be inverted at the output; thus they are applied at the inputs exactly as they are required at the output or exactly as they are written in the equation.

Factoring introduces additional levels of logic and, as was seen in the analysis of NAND gates, may result in additional inverters to compensate for logic entering at an odd level. As in analysis, experience is the best aid toward becoming proficient, because the basic rules are really very simple and once they are understood need only be applied to visualize the results.

Example 5.16 illustrates a three-level problem. The first-level NAND gate is an OR, the second-level NAND is an AND, the third-level NAND is an OR, and so on. This problem requires the term AB to be OR'ed with another term. Thus a 2-input NAND gate is required at the output of the network. The term AB is provided by a second-level, 2-input NAND gate. The second major term is $D(B + \bar{C})$, which also requires a second-level, 2-input NAND gate. However, the term $(B + \bar{C})$ is one input to this second-level gate and must be accomplished by a third-level NAND gate that will act as an OR gate. Because this third-level NAND gate is an OR function and is at an odd level, any inputs to this gate will appear inverted at the output. Therefore the inputs B and C must be the inversion of what is required at the output, and inputs to this third-level gate must be $\bar{B}$ and C so that the term $(B + \bar{C})$ will appear at the output.

EXAMPLE 5.16. $f = AB + D(B + \bar{C})$.

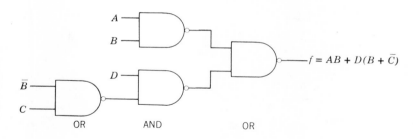

Because any function can be written as a sum of products, any function can be implemented with a two-level implementation. The use of two levels provides the least propagation delay and so is the fastest technique. However, it is often the most expensive in terms of gate count, because the output OR gate must have a fan-in capability equal to the number of OR terms. Example 5.17 illustrates this point. The first implementation of the standard sum form requires four 3-input gates with a 4-input gate at the output. There are two 4-input gates per IC package (assuming the 14-lead flat pack) and three 3-input gates per flat pack. Therefore this implementation requires five gates from two packages. The second implementation requires two 3-input and three 2-input gates. There are four 2-input gates per package and three 3-input gates per package. Therefore this implementation requires only one package of 3-input gates and $\frac{1}{2}$ package of 2-input gates for the five required gates, for a total of $1\frac{1}{2}$ packages.

One important advantage that can be gained by factoring is the elimination of inverters. Example 5.18 illustrates the classic exclusive-OR function. This function is so common that there are multifunctional packages available with the complete logic for implementation of the exclusive-OR. The first implementation in Example 5.18 is straightforward. The second assumes that the complements of the terms A and B are not available and must be generated. This is quite common when it is desirable to carry

EXAMPLE 5.17. $f = \bar{A}B\bar{C} + \bar{A}BD + ACD + A\bar{B}C.$

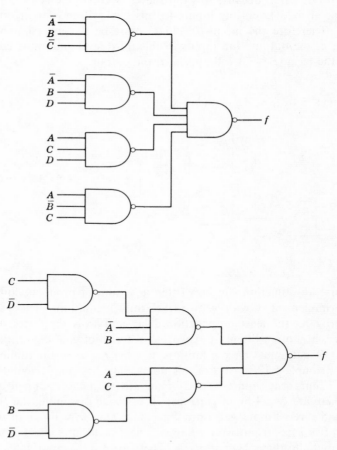

Factoring yields $f = \bar{A}B(\bar{C} + D) + AC(\bar{B} + D).$

EXAMPLE 5.18. $f = A\bar{B} + \bar{A}B$.

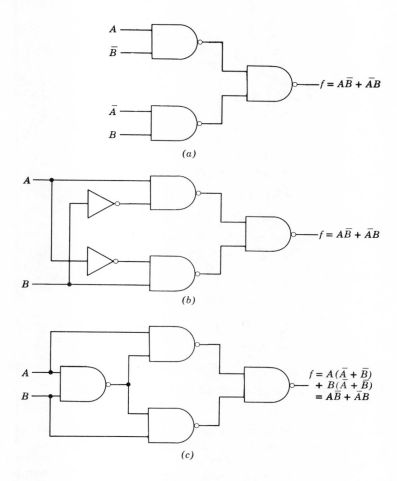

(a)

(b)

(c)

only two wires from one point to another in the system, instead of all four wires. The third implementation is a little more elegant than the others and reduces the number of gates to four. As there are four 2-input gates per package this takes only one package.

It can be seen that the logic is a direct reflection of the equation. Ability to manipulate the equation is required if various forms of a function are to be inspected. It should be obvious that the minimum algebraic expression is certainly not the only form implemented. Part c of Example 5.18, for instance, results in a rather complex expression for a very simple function.

Figure 5.22 shows a Karnaugh map of a sample function. Listed below the

DC \ AB	00	01	11	10
00	0	0	1	1
01	1	1	0	1
11	1	1	0	1
10	0	0	1	1

(f)

$$f = \bar{A}D + A\bar{D} + \bar{B}D \qquad (1)$$

$$f = (A + D)(\bar{A} + \bar{B} + \bar{D}) \qquad (2)$$

$$f = (A + D)(\bar{A} + \bar{D}) + \bar{B}D \qquad (3)$$

$$f = A(\bar{A} + \bar{D}) + D(\bar{A} + \bar{D}) + \bar{B}D \qquad (4)$$

$$f = A(\bar{A} + \bar{D}) + D(\bar{A} + \bar{D} + \bar{B}) \qquad (5)$$

$$f = A\bar{D} + D(\bar{A} + \bar{D} + \bar{B}) \qquad (6)$$

$$f = \bar{A}\bar{B}D + \bar{A}B\bar{D} + A\bar{C}\bar{D} + AC\bar{D} + A\bar{B}D \qquad (7)$$

$$f = \bar{A}(\bar{B}D + B\bar{D}) + A(\bar{C}\bar{D} + C\bar{D} + \bar{B}D) \qquad (8)$$

$$f = \bar{A}(B + D)(\bar{B} + \bar{D}) + A(\bar{D} + \bar{B}D) \qquad (9)$$

$$f = (A + C + D)(A + \bar{C} + D)(\bar{A} + \bar{B} + \bar{D}) \qquad (10)$$

Figure 5.22 Different equations for the same function.

map are no less than 10 different expressions that represent the function, and this is by no means all the expressions that could be written. Many of these are minimal expressions and many contain redundant terms, but they are all equally valid expressions and require different logic implementation.

NOR logic follows the same procedure as NAND logic except that the odd-even levels start with an AND gate as the output and then alternate as OR-AND-OR-AND-.... Thus the standard product of sum form is indicative of NOR logic. In Figure 5.22 Equations 1 and 7 are sum of products whereas Equations 2 and 10 are product of sums. Figure 5.23 illustrates the implementation of the exclusive-OR function with NOR logic. It can be seen that the four NOR gate implementation does not eliminate the complemented inputs but does reduce the number of inputs to two, so that a two-wire signal is all that is required.

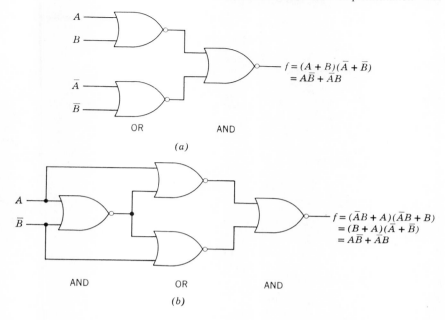

Figure 5.23 Exclusive-OR, NOR logic; $f = A\bar{B} + \bar{A}B$.

The same basic rules of logic implementation exist whether the logic gates are NAND gates or NOR gates. A two-logic-level implementation has the least propagation delay. Factoring usually reduces fan-in requirements while increasing the number of logic levels. This can result in fewer package count, because there are four 2-input gates in a single package but only one 8-input and two 4-input gates per package. It is not wise to spend too much time trying to optimize logic implementation in the development phase of engineering; engineering time is expensive whereas logic gates are cheap. In other words, a logic designer's time may be worth $200 a day. If logic gates cost $1.00 each it certainly is not practical for the designer to spend much time trying to minimize the implementation of a given function, unless enough of a given function is required to justify the time.

PROBLEMS

1. Analyze the following, first writing equation and then mapping:

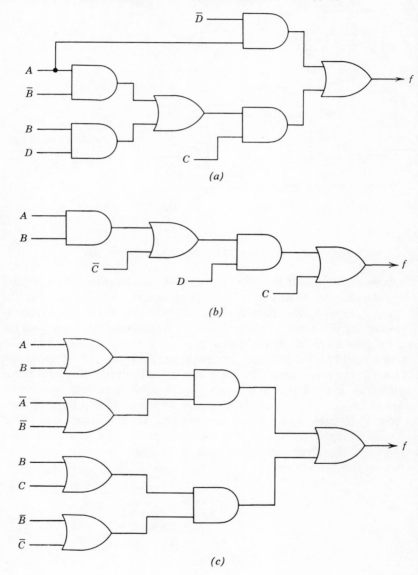

(a)

(b)

(c)

2. Analyze and implement minimal function *a*, *b*:

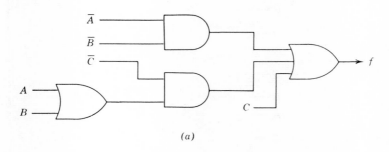

(a)

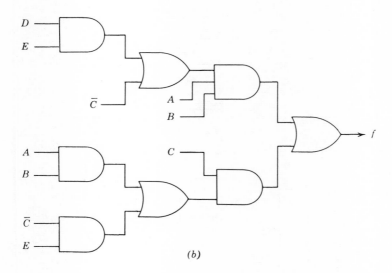

(b)

2. Analyze and implement minimal function c, d:

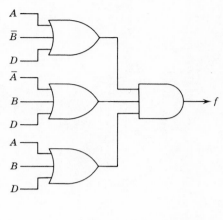

(c)

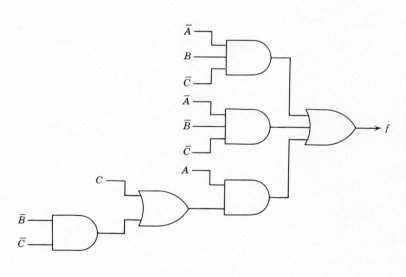

(d)

3. Analyze, writing equation and mapping function:

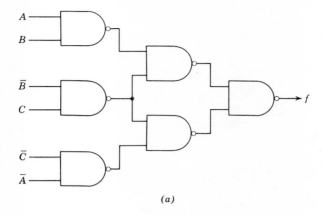

(a)

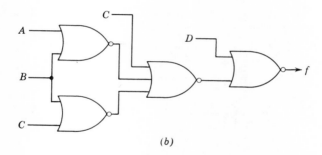

(b)

4. Analyze:

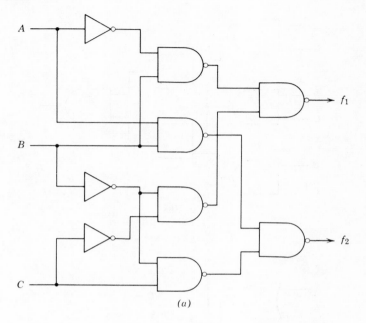

(a)

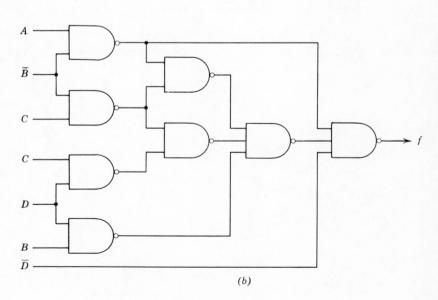

(b)

5. Implement a full adder:

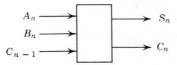

6. Design a combinational network that will preset a flip-flop to the state of a data line input on command of a strobe pulse. Use the S_D and R_D input control functions. These are the d-c set and reset inputs. When the strobe pulse occurs, if the data line is 1, the S_D input to the flip-flop should be 1; if the data line is 0, the R_D input to the flip-flop (FF) should be 1.

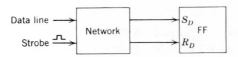

7. Given two inputs, A and B, it is required to have three outputs such that

$$f_1 = A < B$$

$$f_2 = A = B$$

$$f_3 = A > B.$$

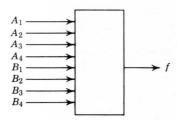

8. Design a network that will indicate when two 4-bit binary numbers are equal. Define A_1 and B_1 as the LSB of the 4-bit numbers. Minimum logic package count is the goal. Inverted inputs are not available.

A_1 →
A_2 →
A_3 →
A_4 →
B_1 →
B_2 →
B_3 →
B_4 →
→ f

6

SEQUENTIAL NETWORKS

Sequential networks are circuits whose output depends not only on the inputs at a given period of time but also on the prior sequence of inputs. Sequential networks follow a programmed sequence that is dependent on the output as well as the input. This is classically illustrated in Figure 6.1 as a logic network with 3 inputs and 1 output. Thus the output must affect the operation of the network and be a factor in determining the state of the output.

6.1 ANALYSIS

In order to analyze a network of this type it is necessary to recognize that events do not take place instantaneously. That is, the output state is delayed somewhat from the change in state of the inputs. In relay networks the delay is referred to as the time it takes for the relay to pull in after energization. This delay period in relay networks can be many milliseconds. In the case of digital integrated circuits the delay time can be very small, a few nanoseconds. Small as it may be it is still a real factor that must be con-

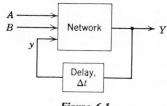

Figure 6.1.

118

sidered. Figure 6.2a shows a combinational network implemented with three NAND gates. If each logic gate had a 20-nsec propagation delay the total delay of the network would be that of two gates, or 40 nsec. It is expected, therefore, that the output would change state 40 nsec after a change in state of the inputs. Figure 6.2b shows this delay, Δt, lumped at the output. The intent is to consider the point of output Y as the excitation point and the point labeled y as the response to the excitation after the required delay. This lumping of delays is a subterfuge to allow combinational logic techniques to be applied to sequential logic. It allows the point Y to be analyzed as $Y = AB + BC$, a combinational network. Then, after an appropriate period of time, $y = Y$. This network is simple, and the output Y is certainly dependent on the state of the inputs A, B, and C at any given period of time. Analysis of Figure 6.2a reveals that if all inputs are low the output is low. If B goes high nothing happens at the output until either A or C also goes high, as shown in Figure 6.3. But the output is delayed by Δt, the propagation delay of the network.

If it is assumed this delay is lumped, as shown in Figure 6.2b, the output state Y is determined the instant the inputs change, and the period until the

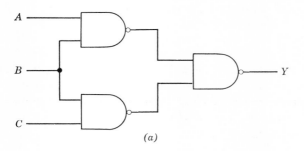

(a)

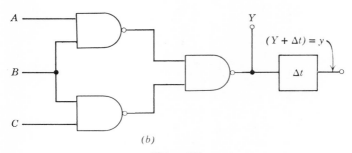

(b)

Figure 6.2.

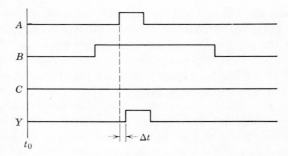

Figure 6.3.

response to this excitation is complete is only Δt. Figure 6.4 is the same net-work, but with the response y serving as the input C. Thus $Y = AB + By$, as before for a combinational network. Figure 6.5 is a timing diagram for this network and shows a significant difference from the timing diagram of Figure 6.3. In Figure 6.3 the output remained high only as long as A was high, whereas in Figure 6.5 the output goes high with the change in state of A and remains high as long as B is high even though A comes down. As in the combinational network the output Y goes high when A and B are high but the output is fed back after a time period, Δt, to serve as a latch and hold the output Y high after A comes down. If combinational techniques were used to analyze the network of Figure 6.6a, it would be as shown in the map of Figure 6.6b. This map has a 1 entry in the cells representative of A and B equal to 1 and in the cells representative of B and y equal to 1. All other cells contain 0. Thus the entries in the cells reflect the logical state of the output Y. This particular map is called the excitation matrix, just as

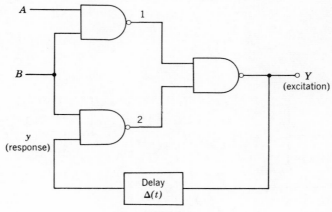

Figure 6.4.

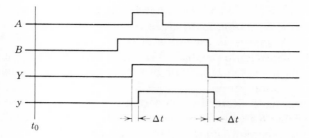

Figure 6.5 Timing diagram.

the state of Y was earlier referred to as the excitation of the network. If the excitation is equal to the response, y, the network is said to be stable. If the excitation is not equal to the response, the network is said to be unstable. Inputs A and B are from an external source and are referred to as control inputs. Once the network is stable nothing can change unless a change occurs in the control inputs. The control inputs are listed across the top of the excitation matrix. Thus a change in control inputs is a horizontal movement

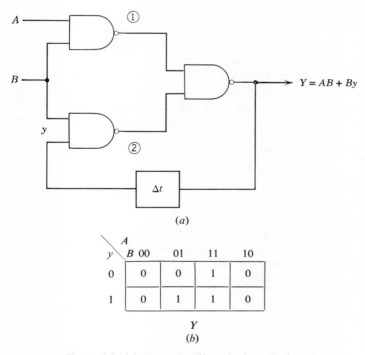

$Y = AB + By$

(a)

y \ $\begin{matrix}A\\B\end{matrix}$	00	01	11	10
0	0	0	1	0
1	0	1	1	0

Y

(b)

Figure 6.6 (a) Network; (b) excitation matrix.

in the matrix of Figure 6.6b. A change in the control inputs, a horizontal movement in the excitation matrix, can result in an excitation or change in the output Y. A change in excitation of the output will result in a vertical movement in the excitation matrix. Vertical transitions within a column of the matrix indicate a change in state of the output. A change in state is an unstable or transition period.

This may be made clearer by comparing the various states of the timing diagram of Figure 6.5 with the excitation matrix of Figure 6.6b At t_0 inputs A and B are 0. Therefore node ① of Figure 6.6a is a logic 1. Because B is 0, node ② must also be 1, independent of what y is. As ① and ② are both 1, the output Y is 0. Assuming that sufficient time has passed since any change in state occurred, y must be the same as Y and is therefore 0. This is represented as the period t_0 in the timing diagram and as the 0 entry in the $A = B = y = 0$ cell. The next event is when B goes to 1 in the timing diagram. This is equivalent to a horizontal movement from $A = B = 0$ to $A = 0$, $B = 1$, or from 00 to 01 in the excitation matrix. The entry for Y in this cell is 0. Thus no change in the state of Y occurs. This is compatible with the network because, if $A = 0$, node ① $= 1$ and, because $y = 0$, node ② $= 1$ and the output Y must remain 0. Because Y remains 0, a change in state of Y has not occurred and y will remain 0. The network is still stable.

The next event in the timing diagram is when A goes to 1. This is a horizontal transition from 01 to the column 11. Combinational analysis resulted in a 1 in the first row of this column. This signifies that the output Y has now changed state from 0 to 1. This agrees with analysis, because if both A and B are 1 then node ① must be 0. If node ① is 0, the output Y must be 1. The top cell signifies that a horizontal transition from a 01 state to a 11 state has resulted in excitation of Y. An unstable state now exists. Y has gone to 1, but the time period Δt has not elapsed. This unstable state is represented by the excitation of Y to 1 while the feedback, y, is still 0. A vertical transition in the 11 column of excitation matrix now takes place. y must change state from 0 to 1 in the time period Δt. This is illustrated in the timing diagram, where y goes to 1 after Y. This transition in the excitation matrix is from the top cell in the 11 column, where y (on the left) is 0, to the bottom cell, where y (on the left) is 1. Analysis of this new state, where node ① is 0, forces Y to be 1 independent of node ②. Thus this is a new stable state. The excitation matrix agrees with this, because the vertical movement has produced a state of Y that agrees with the state of y. That is, Y is 1 and now y is 1.

To continue the analysis of the network and the timing diagram in Figure 6.5, the next event is when A goes to 0. The present state is represented by the $A = B = y = 1$ cell, and so a change of A from 1 to 0 is represented by a horizontal transition from the 11 to the 01 column. This change in state of A causes node ① to go from 0 to 1. But, because $B = y = 1$ and node

② = 0, a change in state of A will not produce any change in the output Y. Because Y does not change state, y does not change and the system is still stable. Figure 6.7 traces these movements through the matrix. The feedback y now serves as a latch to hold the output high independent of A. That is, A can now change state from 1 to 0 and 0 to 1 without affecting the output. This is equivalent to a horizontal movement from 01 to 11 to 01 in the bottom row of the matrix.

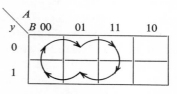

Figure 6.7.

The last event is for B to go from 1 to 0 while A is 0. This represents the transition from 01 to 00. If A and B are both 0 the output Y must be 0. But, because Y was 1 and has now changed to 0, another unstable state exists because y is still 1. Therefore a vertical movement in the matrix must take place during Δt so that y becomes equal to Y. Analysis of the network will show this to be a stable state. A sequence of events has now taken place. This sequence can be described as one in which the output will go to 1 when A goes to 1 provided that B is 1 and will remain 1 until B returns to 0. This sequence closes a loop of events and can be repeated.

Another way of illustrating the characteristics of this network is with the transition matrix in Figure 6.8a and the flow matrix in Figure 6.8b. In the transition matrix each cell representing a stable state contains a small circle.

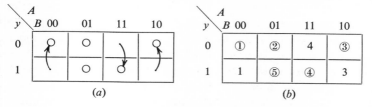

(a)   (b)

Figure 6.8 (a) Transition matrix; (b) flow matrix.

Each cell representative of an unstable state contains a dot. An arrow is drawn from each unstable state to the cell containing the stable state in which the transition will stop. In other words the stable and unstable states are identified. In addition the transition from an unstable to a stable state is illustrated. The flow matrix in Figure 6.8b is extremely useful because it classifies each stable state or cell by a number enclosed in a circle. Each unstable state or cell contains an uncircled number of the stable state to which it will go. If we retrace the sequence of events of the timing diagram in Figure 6.5 for the network in Figure 6.6a, an inspection of the flow matrix in Figure 6.8b indicates that the sequence of events starts with stable state ①.

The change in control inputs of B from 0 to 1 is a horizontal shift to stable state ②. The change in control inputs of A to 1 is a horizontal shift to unstable 4. Unstable 4 requires a vertical shift to stable 4 while the control inputs remain steady. The next change in control inputs is when A returns to 0. This is a horizontal shift from stable state ④ to stable state ⑤. Finally, the return of B to 0 produces the horizontal shift to unstable 1, which necessitates the vertical shift to state ①. The flow matrix in Figure 6.8b can be considered to be the analysis of the network in Figure 6.6a. The flow matrix identifies all stable and unstable states and depicts the change in state of the network for all possible combinations of change in state of the control inputs.

The procedure for analyzing sequential networks can be summarized as follows:

1. Write the combinational logic equation for the network. This represents the excitation function. Use lower-case letters for the feedback or memory loops.

2. Create the excitation matrix from the above logic equation. This is equivalent to mapping or analyzing a combinational logic network. Arrange the control inputs across the top and the feedback loops along the side. This produces horizontal transitions as a result of a change in the control input, and vertical transitions as a result of feedback.

3. Create the transition matrix by identifying stable and unstable states in the excitation matrix. A stable state is one in which the entry in a given cell (the excitation) is identical with the state of the feedback (the response). That is, referring to Figure 6.6b, if the entry in the cell is 0 and this is the row for $y = 0$, the cell is stable. If the entry is 1 in the row where y is 0, the transition must be to a row where $y = 1$, because the response must be the same as the excitation in order to be stable. Place a circle in the cells that are stable and a dot in the cells that are unstable. Draw an arrow from the unstable cells to the stable cells to indicate direction of transition.

4. Create the flow matrix from the transition matrix by assigning a circled number to each stable state and an uncircled number to each unstable state. The uncircled numbers indicate the stable state to which that unstable state will go. There should be no more numbers than there are stable states, except for special oscillatory cases, which will be illustrated.

EXAMPLE 6.1. *Analyze the sequential network in Figure* 6.9a.

This network has two control inputs, A and B. The output is returned through an inverter to be AND'ed with A and directly returned to be AND'ed with the inverse of B. Thus

$$Y = A\bar{y} + \bar{B}y.$$

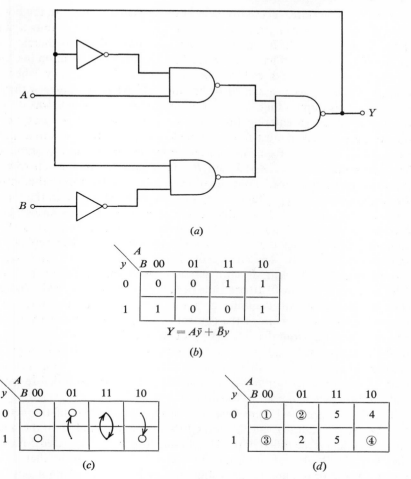

Figure 6.9 (a) Network; (b) excitation matrix; (c) transition matrix; (d) flow matrix.

This is mapped in the normal manner in the excitation matrix of Figure 6.9b with A and B across the top and the single feedback element, y, along the side. Thus entries are 1 in the cells for $A = 1$ and $y = 0$ as well as where $B = 0$ and $y = 1$. All other cells are 0.

The transition matrix, Figure 6.9c, is next completed. The cells identified as stable states in the excitation matrix are identified in the transition matrix by a circle. This corresponds to all cells in which the state of Y is identical with the state of y at the left. Thus in the top row, where $y = 0$, the first and second cells are stable states whereas the last two cells represent a transition state or unstable state. These two cells are identified by a dot. In the bottom row of the excitation matrix the first cell contains a 1 and is thus a stable state. The second cell, in the 01 column, contains a 0 and is therefore unstable. This second cell has been entered by a horizontal transition (a change in control inputs). This cell can be entered horizontally only when any change of the inputs is assumed to be slow relative to a change within the network. This implies that the network, and thus the feedback, was stable in the 1 state prior to entering this unstable state. Because the output Y is now 0 the feedback y must follow by undergoing a vertical shift to a stable 0 state; thus the arrow from the bottom unstable cell to the top stable cell. The last column, where $A = 1$ and $B = 0$, is unstable in the top row and stable in the bottom row. Thus the transition is from the top to the bottom. An inspection of the 11 column reveals an unstable state in both the top and bottom rows. The lack of a stable state in a column indicates an oscillatory condition. Assume a horizontal transition from stable state 2 to the 11 column. This signifies that while B was 1 A went to 1. The network was stable with $Y = y = 0$. The change of A to 1 changes Y to 1 and requires y to go from 0 to 1. But, as soon as y is 1, this signals a change in Y from 1 to 0. Since Y is now 0, after a time period Δt y must be 0. This change in state or oscillation will continue at a rate determined by the delay of the network until one or both of the control inputs, A and B, are changed or power is removed from the network. Notice that if, when $A = B = 1$, A goes to 0 the output will stabilize at 0, whereas if B goes to 0 the output will stabilize at 1. It is impossible for two events to occur at the same instant of time. Therefore the output will stabilize at 0 if A goes to 0 before B, or it will stabilize at 1 if B goes to 0 before A.

The flow matrix in Figure 6.9d summarizes the analysis of the network. It shows stable states ① and ② in the top row with ③ and ④ in the bottom row. A state 5 is identified in the 11 column. The lack of a circled 5 indicates the lack of a stable state and, therefore, the presence of an oscillatory condition. If the programming of A and B is such that they cannot both be 1 at the same time, the oscillation state will never occur.

This network is very useful as a memory or storage device to record which input was last to go high. That is, starting in stable state ①, if A goes high and then back down, signifying a control input transition of $00 \to 10 \to 00$, the output goes to 1 and stays there. Thus the A input could be called a SET input. If B goes high and then low, signifying a control input change of $00 \to 01 \to 00$, the output was originally low and remains low if this change started from stable state ①. However, this transition from stable ③ would change the output from high to low. Thus B always RESETS the output. As long as A and B do not go high at the same time there is no problem.

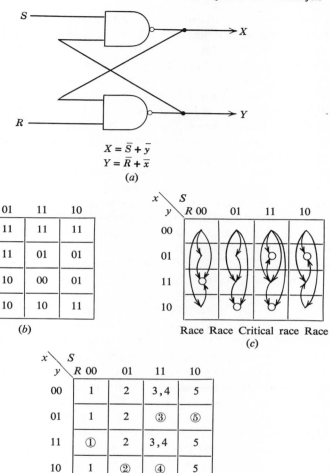

$$X = \bar{S} + \bar{y}$$
$$Y = \bar{R} + \bar{x}$$

(a)

(b)

Race Race Critical race Race

(c)

(d)

Figure 6.10 (a) Network; (b) excitation matrix; (c) transition matrix; (d) flow matrix

EXAMPLE 6.2. *Analyze the network of Figure* 6.10a.

This network represents the simplest type of flip-flop. It is simply two NAND gates cross-coupled on themselves. The equations for both outputs, X and Y, are

$$X = \bar{S} + \bar{y}$$

$$Y = \bar{R} + \bar{x}.$$

This is mapped in the excitation matrix of Figure 6.10*b*. The first entry in each cell corresponds to the state of X, whereas the second entry corresponds to the state of Y. As in the single feedback case, whenever the excitation state of X and the excitation state of Y both agree with the response states of x and y, the network is stable. Thus the transition matrix in Figure 6.10*c* shows a stable state in the first or 00 column and the third or 11 row. This condition signifies that if both S and R are 0 both outputs will be 1. In this particular flip-flop connection of NAND gates, because X and Y should not be in the same state, it is a predetermined requirement that both S and R not be allowed to be 0 at the same time. However, continuing the analysis of the 00 column, the second cell down contains a 11 entry. This indicates that the outputs X and Y have both been excited to the 1 state and that after time period Δt the x and y responses must be the same. Because the excitation and response of Y are the same, there will be no change in state of Y or y; it is 1 and will remain 1. However, the response of X is 0 and the excitation is 1; therefore there must be a vertical transition of X from 0 to 1. This causes a move from the 01 row to the 11 row, where a stable state is reached. The same is true of the bottom cell in the 00 column, except that this time y is the feedback that changes; that is, x remains stable while y goes from 0 to 1. The top cell of the 00 column is different. The excitation of both X and Y is 1 whereas the response of both x and y is 0. The finite delays or response time of each path will determine which changes state first. The excitation is 11, and the responses are 00 and are directed to a 11 state. X and Y may get to the 11 state by $11 \rightarrow 11$ directly if both change state simultaneously. If x changes before y the transition will be to the 10 row. From the 01 row the responses are still directed to 11; therefore the transition will eventually be to the 11 state. That is, from the unstable 00 row, the transition will be $00 \rightarrow 10 \rightarrow 11$. The final possibility is for y to change first, causing a transition of $00 \rightarrow 01 \rightarrow 11$. This is a *race* condition, because the stable state is obtained only after a race between two variables that have been required to change state at the same time. It is a *noncritical* race, however, because the same stable state is reached regardless of the path followed.

An analysis of the 01 column reveals a similar situation. There is only one stable state and thus, regardless of the races, the network will always stabilize at the stable state, where $X = 1$ and $Y = 0$. Again a noncritical race condition exists in the 00 row, because both variables are programmed to change state simultaneously.

Inspection of the 10 column indicates that a stable state exists only in the 01 row. All other cells in this column are unstable; however, any vertical race will stabilize in the 01 row; thus the noncritical race condition again.

The 11 column presents a different case. There is a stable state in the 01 row and the 10 row since the excitation of X and Y agrees with the response states of x and y. The top cell in this column again requires a double change. The present 00 state may go from 00 to 10, or from 00 to 01, or from 00 to 11. All of these possibilities must be accounted for as before. Examining each of these possibilities reveals that the network could end up in two entirely different stable states. If the transition is from 00 to 01, the network will stop there as this is a stable state. If the transition is from 00 to 10, again the network will stop here because this is also a stable state. This is therefore a *critical race*, because the stable state reached is dependent on which feedback loop occurs first. This critical race condition also is present in the 11 row because again the program calls for two variables to change state simultaneously. There is the rare possibility of an oscillation occurring if both variables do change state instantaneously; that is, the oscillation $00 \rightarrow 11 \rightarrow 00 \rightarrow 11 \rightarrow \dots$.

This simple little network thus is full of all kinds of excitement. The flow matrix in Figure 6.10*d* completes the analysis and shows the critical race condition by entering uncircled 3 and 4 in the two cells where the critical race condition exists.

The actual use of this network requires that restrictions be imposed on the inputs; that is, both inputs cannot be low or a logic 0 at the same time. This prevents use of the 00 column for S-R and restricts the operation to the stable states ②, ④ and ③, ⑤. Notice that there is no stable state in the 00 row; therefore a horizontal transition, or change in control inputs, will not result in vertical transitions to or from this row. And, because the 00 state for S-R is prohibited, stable state ① will not occur. Therefore horizontal transitions cannot occur from state ①. This narrows the normal operation of this network from stable state ③ through state ② to state ④, and from state ④ through state ⑤ to state ③. This program is a safe, well-defined sequence of events and results in a very practical circuit.

6.2   SYNTHESIS

Although the prime objective of analysis is to understand the operation of a network, the objective of synthesis is to create a network as a result of some desired sequence of events or required operation. This should necessitate a reversal of the order of methods from that used in analysis. That is, whereas analysis started with a network and ended with a flow matrix, synthesis should start with something like a flow matrix in order to end with a network. This is essentially true except that a few more tricks are required to create the flow matrix. Once a flow matrix has been created it is a relatively simple matter to create the network.

Synthesis starts with a clear, concise statement of the required program or sequence of events. A primitive flow table is created to account for all possible combinations of inputs and desired outputs. From this primitive flow table various techniques are used to achieve a minimum flow table that requires the least number of feedback networks so that assignments can be made to achieve a minimum network implementation. Some examples will illustrate the procedure.

EXAMPLE 6.3. *Design a sequential network that will count up to four change in states of an input as shown in Figure* 6.11.

The network has a single input, A, and two outputs, Z and Z_2, for each of the four sequential inputs as shown in the timing diagram.

The first step is to develop a *primitive flow table*. This table is used to define the outputs required for all possible sequences or combinations of sequences of the input and output. Figure 6.12 shows the primitive flow table in successive stages of development. All possible combinations of the input are listed across the top of the table. Because there is only one input, A, in this problem the only listing across the top is for the case when A is 0 and 1. A column is formed at the right to list the desired output states as a result of the input sequence. A start must be made somewhere, so, referring to the timing diagram in Figure 6.11b, when input A is 0, the outputs Z_1 and Z_2 are in the 00 state. Therefore a stable state ① is defined, as a start, with an output of $Z_1 = Z_2 = 0$. This is shown in Figure 6.12a. Referring to the same figure, when A goes from 0 to 1 it is desired that a new output occur, that of $Z_1 = 0$ while $Z_2 = 1$. This new output requires a new stable state.

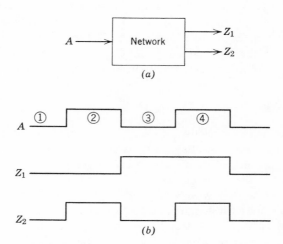

Figure 6.11 (a) Network; (b) timing diagram.

Input A		Ouptut	
0	1	Z_1	Z_2
①	2	0	0
	②	0	1

(a)

Input A		Output	
0	1	Z_1	Z_2
①	2	0	0
3	②	0	1
③		1	0

(b)

Input A		Output	
0	1	Z_1	Z_2
①	2	0	0
3	②	0	1
③	4	1	0
	④	1	1

(c)

Input A		Output	
0	1	Z_1	Z_2
①	2	0	0
3	②	0	1
③	4	1	0
1	④	1	1

(d)

Figure 6.12 Primitive flow table.

Thus the entry in the flow table of Figure 6.12a, when moving horizontally from $A = 0$, stable state ①, to $A = 1$, is an unstable 2. A new row is now created with the entry ② for a stable state 2 and a new output is shown for this stable state. In the development of the primitive flow table a new row is created for each new stable state. The output may or may not change, depending on requirements. From stable ② the next change must be for A to go from 1 to 0. This is a horizontal transition in the table and requires a new unstable state, 3. A new row must be added to the table to list stable ③ with a new output of 10. This is shown in Figure 6.12b. This process continues until all required transitions are accounted for with required outputs defined as shown in Figure 6.12a–d. After stable state ④, when A returns to 0 the output is to repeat and returns to 00. This signals the end of the table and closes the sequence by returning to stable state ①. This is a very simple table and is now completely defined. There are four stable states requiring two feedback or memory elements to define the four required states. That is, it takes two binary variables to define four different states. Therefore the next step is to establish the combinational assignments that these feedback loops should take. Such things as oscillations and races in the flow matrix should generally be avoided. This implies a requirement to allow only one variable to change at a time. A letter assignment to the stable states of the

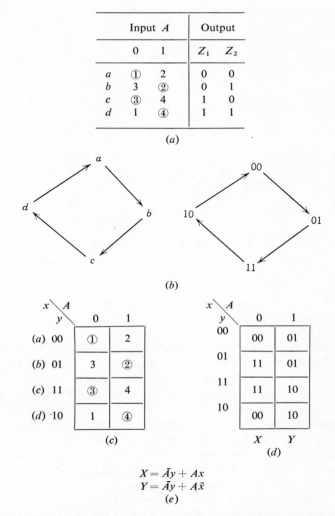

	Input A		Output	
	0	1	Z_1	Z_2
a	①	2	0	0
b	3	②	0	1
c	③	4	1	0
d	1	④	1	1

(a)

(b)

$x \backslash A$		
y	0	1
(a) 00	①	2
(b) 01	3	②
(c) 11	③	4
(d) 10	1	④

(c)

$x \backslash A$		
y	0	1
00	00	01
01	11	01
11	11	10
10	00	10
	X	Y

(d)

$$X = \bar{A}y + Ax$$
$$Y = \bar{A}y + A\bar{x}$$
(e)

Figure 6.13 (a) Flow table; (b) transition diagram; (c) flow matrix; (d) excitation matrix; (e) equations.

flow table in Figure 6.13a is used to create the transition diagram in Figure 6.13b. This transition diagram shows that a change in the input requires a to go to b, or signals that a should be adjacent to b relative to changes in the feedback variables. To put it another way, it is desirable that a one-variable change in the feedbacks cause a transition from state ① to state ②. It seems reasonable, therefore, that the Gray code assignment be made to the feedback loops as shown. This assignment, called the *secondary assignment*, results in the flow matrix of Figure 6.13*c*. Two feedback loops, *x* and *y*, have now been identified. The flow matrix has four stable states identified as well as all unstable states. There are no blank cells, signifying that all states have been accounted for. This flow matrix results in the excitation matrix of Figure 6.13*d*. The entries in the excitation matrix must comply with the requirements of the flow matrix as to stable and unstable entries. It becomes the program for the network, and the Boolean equations for *X* and *Y* are taken directly from the excitation matrix by grouping the 1's (or the 0's) and writing minimal expressions as shown. Figure 6.14 is an implementation of the equations for *X* and *Y* using two inverters and five 2-input NAND gates.

There is one thing yet to be done, however, and that is to provide the outputs Z_1 and Z_2. These outputs are obtained by defining the output state for each stable state in the sequential network. The outputs were defined by the problem in the timing diagram of Figure 6.11*b*. They were listed in the primitive flow tables of Figure 6.12 and the final flow table of Figure 6.13*a*. Using the flow matrix of Figure 6.13*c* as a reference, an output matrix is prepared that defines the states required of Z_1 and Z_2 for each

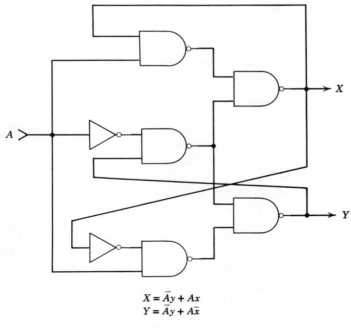

$$X = \bar{A}y + Ax$$
$$Y = \bar{A}y + A\bar{x}$$

Figure 6.14.

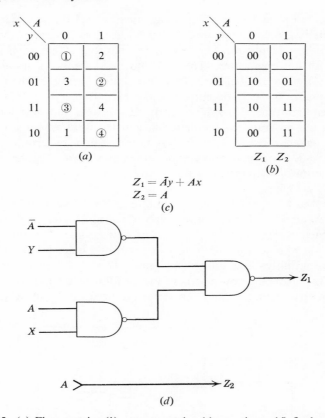

$$Z_1 = \bar{A}y + Ax$$
$$Z_2 = A$$
(c)

Figure 6.15 (a) Flow matrix; (b) output matrix; (c) equations; (d) final network.

stable state of X and Y. Thus Figure 6.15b represents the desired outputs as a function of all possible combinations of the input and feedback loops. The equations of Figure 6.15c are minimal and result in a maximum grouping of the 1's for Z_1 and Z_2. Note that Z_2 is defined as just A. This agrees with the appearance of Z_2 in the timing diagram, where Z_2 always has the same state as the input A. Figure 6.15d is an implementation of the functions Z_1 and Z_2, and Figure 6.16 combines the implementations to show the complete network. Notice that if the sequence of the outputs Z_1 and Z_2 were made a Gray code sequence the feedback nodes x and y could serve directly as the outputs Z_1 and Z_2 without any additional decoding.

This is certainly not the only network that can be implemented to perform the required function. A simple change in the secondary assignments of Figure 6.13c can result in a vastly more complex network, or one more simple. A change in the secondary assignments can result in a network with

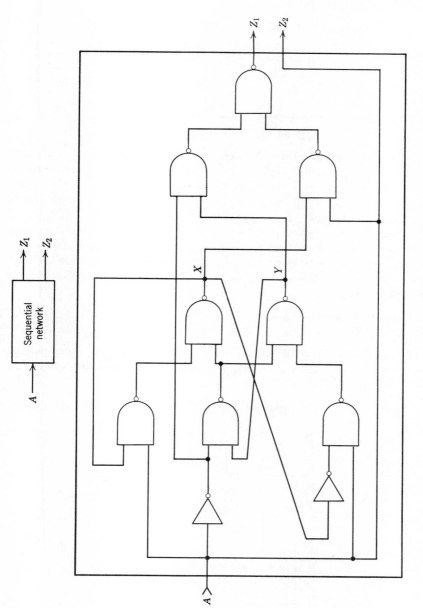

Figure 6.16.

135

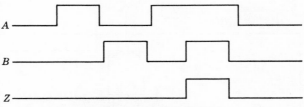

Figure 6.17 Timing diagram.

oscillations or critical race conditions. Needless to say, the secondary assignments are the most demanding part of this procedure. For example, it would be undesirable to make the secondary assignment agree with the state of the outputs as defined, because it would result in a two-variable change in the transition from stable state ② to stable state ③.

Starting a primitive flow table is arbitrary. It is not necessary to start at the point chosen, which was just a convenience. Since sequential networks usually complete a cycle of events, any points can be used to start and will end in a closed cycle. Recognizing the end or completion of a cycle is usually more difficult than finding a place to start.

EXAMPLE 6.4. *Given two inputs, A and B, design a network that will provide an output Z when both inputs are high but only when A goes high before B.*

The output should remain high as long as *B* is high. The inputs can change only one at a time; that is, a double change of the inputs cannot occur (see timing diagram in Fig. 6.17).

The first step is the creation of the primitive flow table in Figure 6.18.

$\begin{array}{c}\quad A\\ B\end{array}$ 00	01	11	10	Z
a	①	5	–	2	0
b	1	–	3	②	0
c	–	4	③	2	1
d	1	④	3	–	1
e	1	⑤	6	–	0
f	–	5	⑥	7	0
g	1	–	6	⑦	0

(a)

(b)

Figure 6.18 (a) Primitive flow table; (b) merger diagram.

One approach is to start with both inputs at 0 and proceed through a proper sequence to obtain an output. This establishes a stable state ① in the first row under the 00 column, with an output of 0. A proper sequence is for A to go to 1. This is a horizontal transition from the 00 column to the 10 column. A new unstable state is created here because, by definition of the primitive flow table, there can be only one stable state in each row. Thus unstable 2 is identified and a new row is created with a stable state ② and a zero output. The next event is for B to go high, causing a transition from the 10 column to the 11 column. This is according to plan and an output is now desired. This sequence is identified by the unstable 3 and the new row containing stable ③ with a 1 output.

This completes the basic requirements of the program, but there is still much to be determined. All possible combinations and sequences of events must be accounted for. From state ③, assumed that A returns to 0 while B remains high. This is a transition from 11 to 01. A new state must be assigned, as there is no stable state for that column. A new row is also assigned for stable state ④ and, because B is still high, the output should remain 1. From stable state ④, if B goes to 0, directing a transition from the 01 column to the 00 column, an unstable 1 is assigned and a loop is closed or a sequence of events is complete.

Other possible transitions must be accounted for. Assume a transition from stable ①, the 00 column, to the 01 column. This transition assumes that A and B are both 0 and that B rises before A. This transition cannot be directed to state 4 because this is not a proper sequence and a 1 output is not desired. Therefore a new state, state 5, is assigned with a zero output. A transition from the 00 to the 11 column will not occur, because the conditions specify that the inputs cannot both change state at the same time. Therefore, in the stable state ① row, a dash is entered under the 11 column. This is equivalent to a ϕ or "don't care" condition in a Karnaugh map. It will be used to simplify the function. In a like manner a dash is entered in all rows where a double change occurs from a stable state. That is, a transition from stable ② to a 01 column cannot occur, and therefore a dash is entered in that row and column. In rows for stable ④ and ⑤ a dash is entered in the 10 column.

Continuing the process, from stable ② assume a transition in which A returns to zero. A return to state ① is desired in order to await another change of A to start the proper sequence. If, from state ④ with B high, A goes high, a return to state 3 is required because the output is to remain high. Once the output has gone high, it will remain high until B goes down. However, from state 5, if A goes high, a new state must be created to provide a 0 output in the 11 column because state 5 was entered by an improper sequence. All possible moves from this new state ⑥ must now be accounted for. From state ⑥, if B goes low, a move to state 2 would be improper because state 2 identifies a correct sequence. Therefore a new state ⑦ must be created and accounted for. States 5, 6, and 7 may be called "holding" states or dummy states because they are created only to account for improper sequences and cause the network to mark time until a proper sequence is initiated. Any return to the 00 column signifies a fresh start and is a return to state 1.

The seven stable states or rows in the primitive flow table would require $2^3 = 8$, or three feedback loops. In dealing with flip-flop programming, many feedback loops can be desirable, as will be shown in Chapter 7. However, in implementing sequential logic with NAND or NOR gates, feedback loops should be minimized. This is accomplished by a procedure known as *merger*. That is, rows within the primitive flow table are merged whenever possible to reduce the number of rows in the flow table in order to reduce the number of required feedback loops. Any two rows in a flow table can be merged (independent of output) provided the state assignments in the columns are identical. For example,

$$\left.\begin{array}{cccc} ① & 3 & 2 & 5 \\ 1 & ③ & - & 5 \end{array}\right\} \rightarrow ① \quad ③ \quad 2 \quad 5.$$

Any dash is replaced by the stable or unstable state, and any unstable state is replaced by a stable state. All possible mergers should be identified so that maximum mergers can be made. The rows of Figure 6.18a have been identified by a lower-case letter, and a merger diagram is shown in Figure 6.18b. This diagram shows the following mergers:

$$
\begin{array}{llcccc}
(a) & ① & 5 & - & 2 \\
& & & & & \left.\right\} \rightarrow ① \quad 5 \quad 3 \quad ② \\
(b) & 1 & - & 3 & ② \\[6pt]
(a) & ① & 5 & - & 2 \\
& & & & & \left.\right\} \rightarrow ① \quad ⑤ \quad 6 \quad 2 \\
(e) & 1 & ⑤ & 6 & - \\[6pt]
(b) & 1 & - & 3 & ② \\
& & & & & \left.\right\} \rightarrow 1 \quad 4 \quad ③ \quad ② \\
(c) & - & 4 & ③ & 2 \\[6pt]
(b) & 1 & - & 3 & ② \\
& & & & & \left.\right\} \rightarrow 1 \quad ④ \quad 3 \quad ② \\
(d) & 1 & ④ & 3 & - \\[6pt]
(c) & - & 4 & ③ & 2 \\
& & & & & \left.\right\} \rightarrow 1 \quad ④ \quad ③ \quad 2 \\
(d) & 1 & ④ & 3 & -
\end{array}
$$

$$
\begin{aligned}
(e) \quad & 1 \quad ⑤ \quad 6 \quad - \\
(f) \quad & - \quad 5 \quad ⑥ \quad 7
\end{aligned}
\Big\} \rightarrow \quad 1 \quad ⑤ \quad ⑥ \quad 7
$$

$$
\begin{aligned}
(e) \quad & 1 \quad ⑤ \quad 6 \quad - \\
(g) \quad & 1 \quad - \quad 6 \quad ⑦
\end{aligned}
\Big\} \rightarrow \quad 1 \quad ⑤ \quad 6 \quad ⑦
$$

$$
\begin{aligned}
(f) \quad & - \quad 5 \quad ⑥ \quad 7 \\
(g) \quad & 1 \quad - \quad 6 \quad ⑦
\end{aligned}
\Big\} \rightarrow \quad 1 \quad 5 \quad ⑥ \quad ⑦.
$$

A line is drawn connecting all points within the merger diagram that can be merged. This shows that a will merge with b and e. Also c will merge with b and d. It shows that e will merge with a, f, and g. A closed triangle, such as bcd and efg, shows a three-way merger.

The next step is to select the most desirable merger. The most desirable merger may or may not be the one that results in the minimum number of rows. Certainly a reduction in the number of rows to four or fewer is desirable, because this would require only two feedback loops instead of three. A reasonable choice is to merge b, c, and d and e, f, and g as shown in the merged flow table of Figure 6.19a. This merged flow table has only three rows and would require $2^2 = 4$, or two feedback loops. The fourth row is not assigned and can be considered a "don't care" row. It is useful, however, in getting from one stable state to another without creating race conditions.

The problem of secondary assignments now presents itself. It is known that there must be two feedback loops, x and y. The state assignment of these variables is not known, however, and so a transition diagram is prepared as an aid in making the secondary assignments. This transition diagram is prepared to determine which rows are adjacent to each other so that an assignment will produce only a one-variable change between adjacent rows. Figure 6.19b shows a transition diagram for the merged flow table by identifying the three merged rows with the letters h, j, and k. This transition diagram is created by inspection of the flow table. Starting with row h,

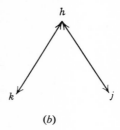

	B 00	01	11	10	
a	①	5	–	2	h
b, c, d	1	④	③	②	j
e, f, g	1	⑤	⑥	⑦	k

(a)   (b)

Figure 6.19 (a) Merged flow table; (b) transition diagram.

state ①, horizontal movement (a change of input variables) will result in a vertical transition to state 5, row k, or state 2, row j. Thus transitions can occur from row h to row j and row k. An arrow is drawn from h to j in the transition diagram. A horizontal shift within row j can only result in a move to row h. Thus an arrow is drawn from j to h. There is no transition between rows j and k. Row k can only move to stable ①, row h.

Thus row h should be adjacent to both rows j and k. The secondary assignment shown in the primitive flow matrix of Figure 6.20a satisfies this

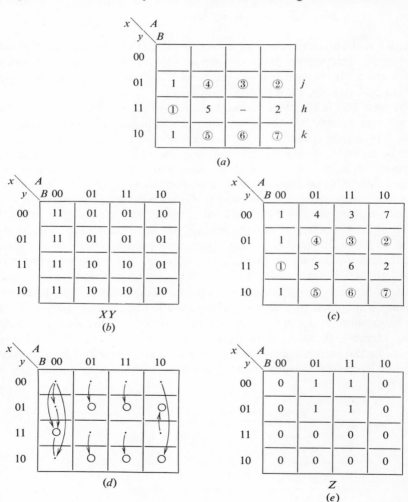

Figure 6.20 (*a*) Primitive flow matrix; (*b*) excitation matrix; (*c*) final flow matrix; (*d*) transition matrix; (*e*) output matrix.

condition by assigning 11 to row h, 01 to row j, and 10 to row k. This leaves the 00 assignment open and allows this row to be used to minimize the implementation and/or eliminate undesired race conditions.

The excitation matrix is next. Entries in the cells must agree with the primitive flow matrix. That is, the entry in the cell for stable state ① must be 11. Entries in the other stable and unstable cells must agree with the established flow requirements. Remaining empty cells are completed to result in a minimum function and/or minimum race conditions. That is, because the 00 column has only one stable state and the output does not change in transitions within this column, an assignment of 11 to the entire

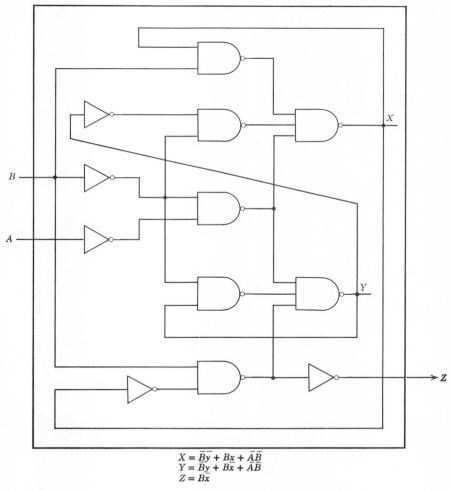

$$X = \overline{B}\overline{y} + Bx + \overline{A}\overline{B}$$
$$Y = \overline{B}y + B\overline{x} + AB$$
$$Z = Bx$$

Figure 6.21.

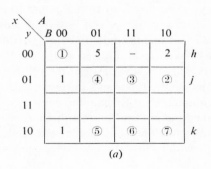

(a)

x \ A y \ B	00	01	11	10	
00	①	5	–	2	h
01	1	④	③	②	j
11					
10	1	⑤	⑥	⑦	k

x \ A y \ B	00	01	11	10
00	00	10	10	01
01	00	01	01	01
11	00	01	01	10
10	00	10	10	10

XY

(b)

x \ A y \ B	00	01	11	10
00	①	5	6	2
01	1	④	③	②
11	1	4	3	7
10	1	⑤	⑥	⑦

(c)

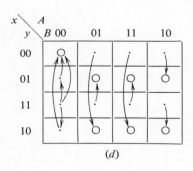

(d)

x \ A y \ B	00	01	11	10
00	0	0	0	0
01	0	1	1	0
11	0	1	1	0
10	0	0	0	0

Z

(e)

Figure 6.22 Alternative assignment: (a) primitive flow matrix; (b) excitation matrix; (c) final flow matrix; (d) transition matrix; (e) output matrix.

142

column seems desirable. A noncritical race condition in this column is acceptable. The remaining entries have been selected to minimize the required implementation. Completion of entries in the excitation matrix results in the final flow matrix in Figure 6.20c. Analysis of this flow matrix will produce the transition matrix in order to illustrate the various transitions. The equations for X and Y result from the excitation matrix and are implemented in Figure 6.21.

The output Z was defined in the primitive flow table. An output matrix, Figure 6.20e, is shown with Z as 1 for stable states ③ and ④. As a minimization, 1 is also assigned to unstable 3 and 4. This produces the equation $Z = B\bar{x}$. As this function is required as part of the sequential network, it is simply brought out to serve as the output through the addition of one inverter. This has illustrated only one secondary assignment that could be made to this problem; Figures 6.22 and 6.23 go through all the necessary steps for the assignment of row h to the 00 row. The different matrices and resulting implementation illustrate the care that must be taken when making secondary assignments.

$$X = B\bar{y} + A\bar{B}x$$
$$Y = By + A\bar{B}\bar{x}$$
$$Z = By$$

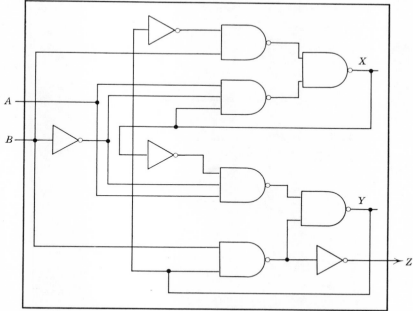

Figure 6.23 Alternative assignment.

PROBLEMS

1. Create a transition matrix and a flow matrix from the following excitation matrix. Identify race conditions as noncritical or critical.

(a)

x A y B	00	01	11	10
00	11	01	10	00
01	11	11	01	01
11	01	11	11	11
10	11	11	10	10

2. Create a flow matrix, a transition matrix, and an excitation matrix from the following equations:

$$X = \bar{A}y + B\mathbf{x} + A(B + \bar{x}\bar{y})$$
$$Y = \bar{B}y + \bar{A}B\bar{x}.$$

3. Analyze the following network; that is, write the equation and create the excitation, transition, and flow matrices:

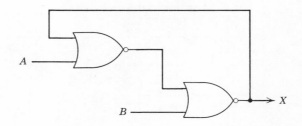

4. Analyze the following network. Expand the flow table and examine for redundant states.

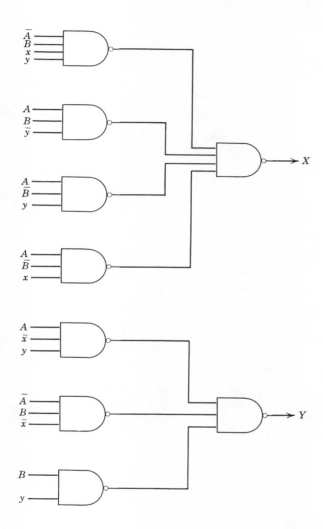

5. Given the primitive flow table below, perform the following functions:
- (a) Identify and remove any equivalencies
- (b) Draw merger diagram
- (c) Perform merger and draw final flow table
- (d) Draw transition diagram
- (e) Make secondary assignments
- (f) Draw excitation matrix, flow matrix, and transition matrix
- (g) Draw output matrix
- (h) Write excitation and output equations

A B 00	01	11	10	Z_1	Z_2
①	2	4	6	0	0
1	②	4	3	0	0
7	5	4	③	0	1
7	5	④	3	0	1
7	⑤	4	6	1	1
7	5	4	⑥	1	0
⑦	5	4	6	1	0
⑧	2	4	6	0	0
7	⑨	4	6	1	1
7	9	⑩	3	0	1

6. Implement the following requirement for a direction sensor. Polarity reversal: Given an encoder that develops two signals, A and B, 90° out of phase with each other. In the CW direction A goes positive before B. In a CCW direction B goes positive before A. Design a sequential network with inputs A and B and an output Z such that $Z = 1$ for CW rotation and $Z = 0$ for CCW rotation. The change of direction should be indicated as soon as possible.

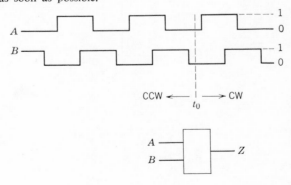

7

PULSED SEQUENTIAL NETWORKS

The sequential networks in the previous chapter were implemented with combinational logic elements, that is, NAND and NOR gates. The networks responded to inputs that occurred asynchronously, and feedback loops or memory elements were held to a minimum.

Pulsed sequential networks are usually composed of flip-flops that are programmed to change state in some orderly sequence as a function of control inputs. The integrated circuit flip-flop has become so versatile and cheap that the requirement to "reduce memory elements in order to reduce costs" is no longer valid. The flip-flop in discrete circuits was not fast, and it often took many combinational logic networks to program each one. The integrated circuit flip-flop, on the other hand, is extremely versatile and easily programmed. This is a result of the complex circuitry that can be fabricated on one small integrated circuit chip.

This section will introduce techniques to analyze and synthesize synchronous flip-flop networks. The networks are synchronous, as one of the control inputs is a pulse and the change in state of the flip-flops is due only to the occurrence of an input pulse. This input pulse will be referred to as the clock pulse, or CP. This does not necessarily mean that the pulses are derived from a stable pulse source; rather, the term clock pulse is used to distinguish it from other pulse-type data. The various types of flip-flops and special programming techniques will be discussed in Chapter 8. The techniques introduced in this chapter can be applied to any type of flip-flop or pulse-controlled network.

7.1 ANALYSIS

As usual, it is easier to analyze a network than to synthesize one. The sample pulsed sequential network that will be analyzed is shown in Figure 7.1; however, some brief explanation of the operation of the flip-flop (FF) is in order.

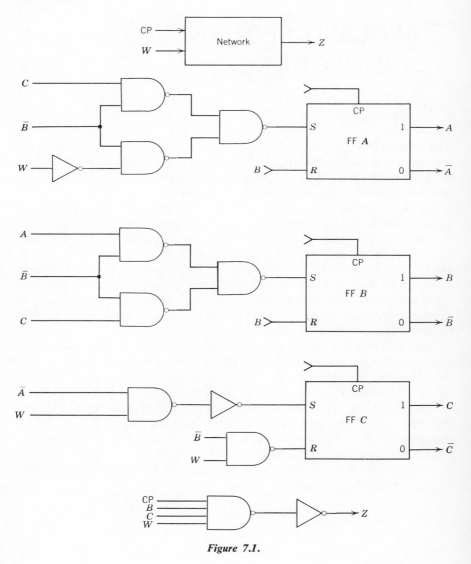

Figure 7.1.

The flip-flop shown has three inputs and two outputs. One input is labeled CP and is the pulse input. The flip-flop changes state only on the occurrence of the input pulse. The state to which the flip-flop goes is determined by the two control inputs, S and R, at the time the CP occurs. The S input is referred to as a "set" input; if it is high when a pulse occurs the flip-flop will "go to" or be set to a 1 state. That is, the output labeled 1 will become 1. The 1 output is referred to as the normal output, whereas the 0 output is referred to as the complement output. The flip-flop is said to be in the 1 state when the 1 output is 1 (at this time the 0 output is 0). The flip-flop is said to be in the 0 state when the 1 output is 0 (at this time the 0 output is 1). This labeling of outputs is required in order to define the "normal" state of the flip-flop. If the R or "reset" input is high the flip-flop will go to or be set to the 0 state when a CP occurs. That is, the output labeled 1 will become 0. This particular type of flip-flop is referred to as an S-R flip-flop. A constraining condition on the inputs S and R is that only one input can be high at any given time; that is, S and R cannot both be 1 at the same time.

If the inputs S and R are both low or 0 when a CP occurs, the flip-flop will not change state; it will remain 1 if it is 1 or it will remain 0 if it is 0. If S is high the FF will go to 1 or remain 1 if it is already 1. If R is high the FF will go to 0 or remain 0 if it is already 0. The network in Figure 7.1 has, in addition to the CP input, only one other input, W. The input W can be referred to as the control or data input. The FFs will change state on command of each CP, and the state to which they will go is determined by their present state and the state of the data input, W. The appearance of a CP on the output line Z, is also a function of the state of the FFs as well as the data input, as can be seen.

The analysis of a pulsed sequential network of this type requires the development of a state diagram. That is, if the FFs are assumed to be in a given state, to what state will they go to on the next CP? The equations for each FF S and R control input must be established. These are obtained from an inspection of the network. The S and R control inputs will be identified by using the letter designation of each FF as a subscript. Thus

$$S_A = \bar{B}C + \bar{B}\,\bar{W}$$

$$R_A = B$$

$$S_B = A\bar{B} + \bar{B}C$$

$$R_B = B$$

$$S_C = \bar{A}W$$

$$R_C = B + \bar{W}$$

$$Z = BCW(\text{CP}).$$

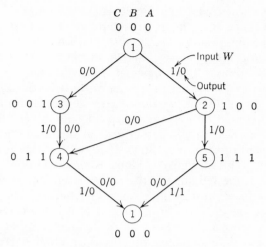

Figure 7.2 State diagram.

An output from the network is obtained when the *B* FF is 1, the *C* FF is 1, and the data input *W* is 1. The state of the *A* FF is not defined at this time. It is usually helpful to determine the conditions necessary to obtain an output and then establish the state of the network after an output is obtained, because this generally signifies the completion of a sequence and the start of a new sequence. If the *B* FF is 1, then inspection of the *S* and *R* inputs to all the FFs will show that the *R* inputs are 1. Therefore the next pulse after *B* goes to 1 will reset all FFs to 0. This would seem to be a desirable starting point. Figure 7.2 shows a state diagram that reflects the sequence of events through which the sample network goes. The first state is identified as state ① in a circle with 000 on top so that, letting *A* be the least significant bit, the state of the three FFs is identified. From state ①, with $A = B = C = 0$, if *W* is ① when the next pulse occurs the FFs go to state ② or a 100 state. This is determined by an examination of the control input equations for each FF.

Given: $A = B = C = 0$, or 000 state, and $W = 1$.

$$S_A = 1 \cdot 0 + 1 \cdot 0 = 0 + 0 = 0$$
$$R_A = 0$$
$$S_B = 0 \cdot 1 + 1 \cdot 0 = 0 + 0 = 0$$
$$R_B = 0$$
$$S_C = 1 \cdot 1 = 1$$
$$R_C = 0 + 0 = 0$$
$$Z = 0 \cdot 0 \cdot 1 = 0.$$

Thus FF A is 0 and remains 0, FF B is 0 and remains 0, FF C is 0 and goes to 1, and the output is 0. This change in state is identified by the arrow from state ① to state ②. State ② is identified as a 100 state. The transition from state ① to state ② is a result of the input W being 1 and does not produce an output; thus the 1/0 along the arrow between states ① and ②.

If while in the 000 state or state ① the input W was 0 when the pulse occurred, the transition would be to state ③ with a 0 output. That is, in state ③

Given: $A = B = C = 0$ and $W = 0$.

$$S_A = 1 \cdot 0 + 1 \cdot 1 = 0 + 1 = 1$$

$$R_A = 0$$

$$S_B = 0 \cdot 1 + 1 \cdot 0 = 0 + 0 = 0$$

$$R_B = 0$$

$$S_C = 1 \cdot 0 = 0$$

$$R_C = 0 + 1 = 1$$

$$Z = 0 \cdot 0 \cdot 0 = 0.$$

Thus the only change is for the A FF to go to 1. This is the 001 state, identified as state ③.

From each state the transition to the next state must be established for all possible variations of the data input. From each state there are two possible transitions, one for $W = 0$ and one for $W = 1$.

From state ③ with $W = 1$ or $A = 1$, $B = 0$, $C = 0$, $W = 1$:

$$S_A = 0$$

$$R_A = 0$$

$$S_B = 1$$

$$R_B = 0$$

$$S_C = 0$$

$$R_C = 0$$

$$Z = 0.$$

The resulting transition is from state ③ to state ④ with a 0 output.

From State ③ with $W = 0$ or $A = 1$, $B = 0$, $C = 0$, $W = 0$:

$$S_A = 1$$

$$R_A = 0$$

$$S_B = 1$$

$$R_B = 0$$

$$S_C = 0$$

$$R_C = 1$$

$$Z = 0.$$

This signals the A FF to go to 1, but it is already 1 and so it will not change state. The B FF is directed to go to 1 and the C FF is directed to go to 0. But the C FF is already 0 and so it will not change state. The output will remain 0. The new state is therefore

Present state	New state
001	011

This is also state ④. Therefore, from state ③, the network will go to state ④ on the next CP regardless of the input state; thus the double notation on the a arrow from state ③ to state ④.

State ② now has to be analyzed to see what the sequence is as a function of the input.

From state ② with $W = 0$, $A = 0$, $B = 0$, $C = 1$:

$$S_A = 1$$

$$R_A = 0$$

$$S_B = 1$$

$$R_B = 0$$

$$S_C = 0$$

$$R_C = 1$$

$$Z = 0.$$

This program calls for FF A to go to 1, B to go to 1 and C to go to 0. The new state is therefore the 011 state with a 0 output. But this is the already identified state ④. Therefore, from state ② with $W = 0$, the transition is to state ④.

State ② with $W = 1$ produces a different transition, with $A = 0$, $B = 0$, $C = 1$:

$$S_A = 1$$
$$R_A = 0$$
$$S_B = 1$$
$$R_B = 0$$
$$S_C = 1$$
$$R_C = 0$$
$$Z = 0.$$

This directs A to go to 1, B to 1, and C to 1, and the output is 0. Thus a new state is identified as state ⑤, the 111 state.

An analysis of transitions from state ④ show that the FFs all return to 0 with the output remaining 0. From state ⑤, however, while the FFs all return to 0 the output goes to 1 if W is 1, and a CP is transmitted to the output.

Examination of the state diagram of Figure 7.2 reveals that an output is generated only for an input sequence of 111. This network is used to step through a sequence for every three input pulse periods and produce a 1 output if the sequence is 111. For any other sequence the output is 0. This is useful in signaling the end of a sequence of transmissions or obtaining a signal in response to this particular code.

The state diagram thus presents a pictorial view into the sequential nature of a network in the same way as the flow matrix. The flow matrix, however, shows all possible combinational states. The state diagram does not necessarily show all possible states or conditions that can occur, only those required by a particular program. The question then arises: What about these undefined states? The previous example contained three FFs. There are eight possible states that can be utilized, but only five were used. What happens, for example, if the three FFs assumed a 101 state when power was applied to the network? An examination of the inputs to each of the three FFs shows that for $A = 1$, $B = 0$, $C = 1$:

$$S_A = 1 \cdot 1 + 1 \cdot \phi = 1$$
$$R_A = 0$$
$$S_B = 1 \cdot 1 + 1 \cdot 1 = 1$$
$$R_B = 0$$
$$S_C = 0 \cdot \phi = 0$$
$$R_C = 0 + \phi = 1 \text{ or } 0.$$

Thus A remains 1, B goes to 1, and C goes to 0 if $W = 1$ or stays 1 if $W = 0$. Therefore, from the 101 state, the network goes to 110 (for $W = 1$) or 111 (for $W = 0$). The 111 state is state ⑤, and so the FFs go into the sequence at state ⑤. The 110 state, however, is another undefined state. Analysis of this state shows that for $W = 0$ the FFs go to the 000 state or state ①. Analysis of the 110 state for $W = 1$ reveals an indeterminate condition. That is, for $A = 0$, $B = 1$, $C = 1$, $W = 1$:

$$S_A = 0$$

$$R_A = 1$$

$$S_B = 0$$

$$R_B = 1$$

$$S_C = 1$$

$$R_C = 1.$$

The C FF now has both S_C and $R_C = 1$. The FF is being directed to go to 1 and 0 at the same time. This is known as an indeterminate condition, because it is not known to which state the FF will actually go. Therefore a ϕ must be written for C because its destination is not known and the network may go to the 100 state or the 000 state. That is, it may go to state ① or state ②, depending on what the C FF does.

One way to avoid this unprogrammed sequence is to preset all FFs to the 0 state before the start of any sequence. In fact, in a sequence of this type, where an examination of three sequential inputs determines an output, the FFs must be set to 0 at the start of the first data input, or an improper result can occur. Thus the requirement to preset the state of the FFs is a condition on the program and must be stated. Otherwise an examination of all unspecified combinational conditions must be carried out in order to understand the operational sequence of the network.

7.2 STATE DIAGRAMS

The development of a state diagram is much the same as the development of a primitive flow table. Combinations of inputs that could not or would not occur are used in a primitive flow table to minimize the number of required states and thus the number of required feedback loops. State diagrams accomplish the same result by simply not analyzing input combinations that do not occur; more specifically state diagrams originate from some required input sequence or program requirement and are not concerned with oscillations or race conditions, because the FFs are programmed for only a fixed routine. Some examples of creating state diagrams will be given to illustrate the point.

EXAMPLE 7.1. *Design a network that will produce an output if the number of 1's contained in a sequence of 3 bits is odd.* That is, if a sequence is 001, 010, 100, or 111, an output should result.

In the beginning of a problem only necessary states are defined. The number of FFs required depends on the number of states required. The programming of the FFs depends on the type of FF selected and the sequence desired. The first step in the development of a state diagram is to assume an initial state and label it as state ①. Figure 7.3*a* shows state ① and states ② and ③, which result from the first input. The arrow from state ① to state ② is labeled 0/0, indicating that the input is 0 and a 0 output is to result. The arrow from state ① to state ③ is labeled 1/0 for a 1 input and the desired 0 output. The moves from state ① to states ② and ③ thus account for the first input being 1 or 0. The second input can also be 1 or 0. No

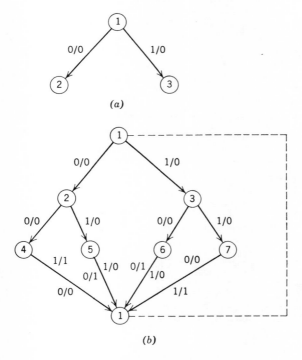

Figure 7.3 Primitive state diagram.

output is required until the third input, so that once again all outputs are labeled 0 as a result of this second input. States ④, ⑤, ⑥, and ⑦ must be created to account for inputs of 1 or 0 from states ② and ③. The next input is the third input, and it is required that (a) a 1 output occur if there is an odd number of 1's and (b) the network return to its initial state to be ready for the next sequence of 3 bits. This is illustrated in Figure 7.3b. The network is directed to return to state ① from states ④, ⑤, ⑥, and ⑦ whether the input is 1 or 0. However, the output certainly depends on whether a 1 or a 0 occurs for the third bit. That is, from state ④, if the sequence has been states ① → ② → ④, then two 0's have occurred so far. The occurrence of another 0 should not produce an output, but the occurrence of a 1 should. Thus, from state ④ to state ①, a 0 input must result in a 0 output or a 0/0

	Next state		Output	
	Input		Input	
Present state	0	1	0	1
1	2	3	0	0
2	4	5	0	0
3	6	7	0	0
4	1	1	0	1
5	1	1	1	0
6	1	1	1	0
7	1	1	0	1

(a)

	Next state		Output	
	Input		Input	
Present state	0	1	0	1
1	2	3	0	0
2	4	5	0	0
3	5	4	0	0
4	1	1	0	1
5	1	1	1	0

(b)

Figure 7.4 (a) Primitive; (b) final state table.

condition. A 1 input must result in a 1 output; thus 1/1. In state ⑤ the sequence has been 01, so that the occurrence of 0 should produce an output whereas the occurrence of 1 will result in two 1's in the sequence, and no output is required.

This completes the required sequence and has defined seven states. However, it seems intuitive that some of these states are not required; that is, some redundancy exists. The primitive state table in Figure 7.4*a* is used to tabulate the states and aid in finding redundant conditions. All seven states are listed in numerical order. The next state is tabulated, along with the desired output, as a function of an input 0 or an input 1. Thus in state ③, if 0 occurs, the next state is state ⑥ with a 0 output. If 1 occurs when in state ③ the next state is state ⑦ with a 0 output. The next state from states ④, ⑤, ⑥, and ⑦ is 1 regardless of the input, but the output is very dependent on the state of the input. Two states may be merged if their next state designations and their output requirements are identical. Thus states ④ and ⑦ are identical and a 4 replaces 7 in the final table with state ⑦ removed. States ⑤ and ⑥ are also identical; thus state ⑥ is a redundant state. Figure 7.4*b* shows the final state table with redundant states removed. This has reduced the number of required states from seven to five, and gives the final state diagram as shown in Figure 7.5.

The network to satisfy this state diagram must contain at least three FFs in order to define five states. Three FFs will provide eight different combinations and so there is an excess of three states in this example. The assignment of combinations to the various required states determines the program for each FF. That is, the assignment of 000 to state ① and 001 to state ② requires a program whereby one of the FFs goes to 1, when the first input is 0, while the other two FFs remain 0. This assignment choice is equivalent to the secondary assignments in sequential networks. The simplicity or complexity of the combinational logic required to perform the programs assigned depends entirely on the cleverness or luck

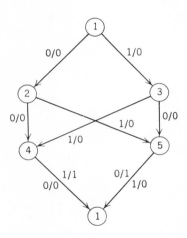

Figure 7.5 Final state diagram.

of the designer. The choice of programs available, even for this simple example, is too large to consider evaluation of them all. Rather, experience and intuition are the best guides. The actual programming of FFs will be covered in the next chapter.

EXAMPLE 7.2. A 4-bit sequential word is to be examined for the occurrence of the decimal 6 or 8. The 4 bits are in BCD (binary-coded decimal) code, and a 6 is represented by the sequence 0110 and an 8 is represented by the sequence 1000. An output is to be provided if either 6 or 8 occurs.

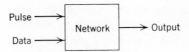

The state diagram is initiated as shown in Figure 7.6a with the initial arbitrary assignment of state ①. From this initial state ① two events can occur when the CP is received: the data input can be 1 or the data input can be 0. Both these conditions are accounted for by creating states ② and ③. If 0 is present the sequence is to state ②, whereas if 1 is present the sequence is to state ③. Once in state ② or ③ the next event may be 1 or 0, which must be accounted for, and this could result in the creation of four new states. However, a little forethought can reduce the possibilities. If the input sequence is 0-1 or 1-0 it may be the beginning of a required sequence; however, if the sequence has been 0-0 or 1-1 it cannot be a correct sequence and so state ⑤ is created as the beginning of a sequence to mark time until the correct number of pulses has gone by, as shown in Figure

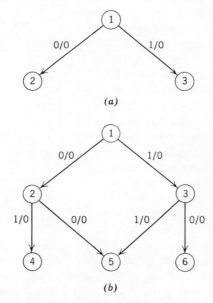

Figure 7.6 Primitive state diagrams.

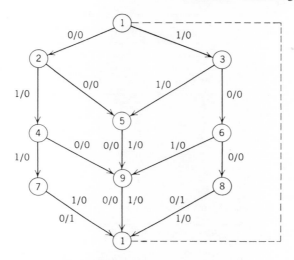

Figure 7.7 Primitive state diagram.

7.6b. The occurrence of 1 or 0 must be accounted for from each state. In state ④, if 1 occurs, this may be a proper sequence and so state ⑦ is created in Figure 7.7. From state ④, the occurrence of 0 signals an improper sequence, and so state ⑨ is created as a holding state. Because state ⑤ is already an incorrect sequence the next pulse should direct the network to state ⑨ regardless of the presence of 1 or 0. State ⑥ accounts for a 1-0 sequence, and a 0 should be recorded as a possible correct number; state ⑧ provides this pattern. A 1 from state ⑥ is an incorrect sequence, and so state ⑨ is adequate without the creation of a new state.

Following the state diagram of Figure 7.7, a 0110 sequence directs the network through states ①, ②, ④, ⑦, and back to ① with a 1 output. A sequence of 1000 progresses through states ①, ③, ⑥, ⑧, and back to ① with a 1 output. Any other sequence uses states ⑤ and ⑨ to mark time and count the four pulses. Figure 7.8a is a state table for the diagram of Figure 7.7, and Figure 7.8b is a reduced state table. An examination of the primitive state table indicates that states ⑦ and ⑧ can be combined because their next states and outputs are identical. Thus the reduced state table in Figure 7.8b contains only eight states, with state ⑦ replacing state ⑧. Remember that considerable reduction was done intuitively in the development of the state diagram. Figure 7.9 shows the completed state diagram resulting from the reduced state table. This final diagram shows that a proper sequence of 0110 goes through ①-②-④-⑦-① with a 1 output and a proper sequence of 1000 goes through ①-③-⑥-⑦-① with a 1 output. Any other sequence uses states ⑤ and/or ⑨.

Present state	Next state		Output	
	Input		Input	
	0	1	0	1
1	2	3	0	0
2	5	4	0	0
3	6	5	0	0
4	9	7	0	0
5	9	9	0	0
6	8	9	0	0
7	1	1	1	0
8	1	1	1	0
9	1	1	0	0

(a)

Present state	Next state		Output	
	Input		Input	
	0	1	0	1
1	2	3	0	0
2	5	4	0	0
3	6	5	0	0
4	9	7	0	0
5	9	9	0	0
6	7	9	0	0
7	1	1	1	0
9	1	1	0	0

(b)

Figure 7.8 (a) Primitive state table; (b) reduced state table.

7.3   SECONDARY ASSIGNMENTS

Pulsed sequential networks utilize flip-flops for programming and assign a different combinational state of the flip-flops for each state in the state diagram. Thus a two-state state diagram could be accounted for by the 1 and 0 states of a single FF. Four states could be accounted for by two FFs, and up to eight states can be accounted for with three FFs. In general m states require n FFs, where $2^n \geq m$. The assignments of the states

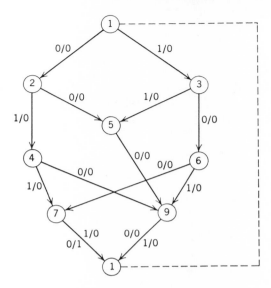

Figure 7.9.

is completely arbitrary and subject mostly to the experience, skill, and intuition of the programmer. Because each FF is individually programmed, there are no race or oscillatory conditions and the designer has complete freedom of choice in the assignments. However, some sequences will be more obvious than others and some combinations of sequences are trivial relative to other combinations.

The sequence chosen determines the simplicity or complexity of the logic network. Thus it may pay to investigate several possible sequences for a particular requirement. Although the actual programming of the FFs resulting from a particular assignment will be covered in the next chapter, a few brief inspections of secondary assignments will be worth while here.

Figure 7.10a shows the state diagram of Example 7.1 with secondary assignments. Because there are five states at least three FFs are required. Thus each state has its own unique combinational conditions of the three FFs. Figure 7.10b shows the state table with the FF states and the next state dependent on the input. This type of table is used in Chapter 8 to develop the combinational network required for each FF in order to have it follow the required sequence. That is, in state ① with all FFs 0, if the data input is 1 the next state is state ③, which has been assigned the 010 combination. This means that the A FF remain 0, the B FF goes to 1, and the C FF remains 0. If, however the data input is 0 from state ①, the next state is ②, where the

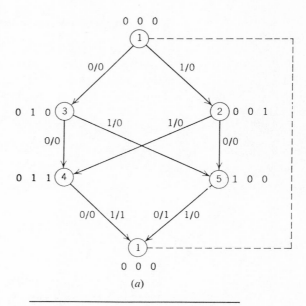

(a)

Present state				Next state	
	FFs			Input	
	C	B	A	0	1
1	0	0	0	010	001
2	0	0	1	100	011
3	0	1	0	011	100
4	0	1	1	000	000
5	1	0	0	000	000
–	1	0	1	–	–
–	1	1	0	–	–
–	1	1	1	–	–

(b)

Figure 7.10 (a) State diagram; (b) secondary assignment.

State	Secondary assignments			
1	000	000	000	000
2	001	010	001	010
3	010	100	011	100
4	011	101	111	110
5	100	111	100	111

Figure 7.11 Secondary assignments.

162

combination is 001. This means that the next state for the A FF is 1 while the B and C FFs remain 0. Other possible secondary assignments are shown in Figure 7.11. The final determination of the simplicity of the selected assignment cannot be made until the type of FFs is selected and the required logic examined.

PROBLEMS

1. Analyze the pulse sequential network below. The characteristic table for the J-K FF is given.

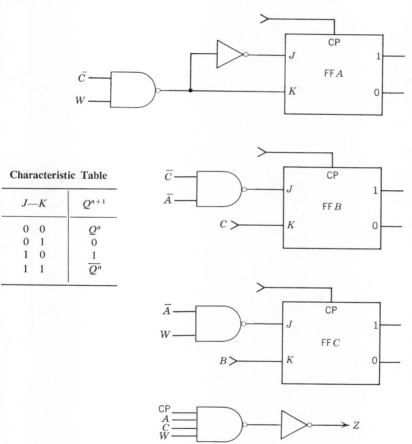

Characteristic Table

J—K		Q^{n+1}
0	0	Q^n
0	1	0
1	0	1
1	1	$\overline{Q^n}$

2. Analyze the following counter network. The *J-K* FFs characteristic table is the same as for Problem 1.

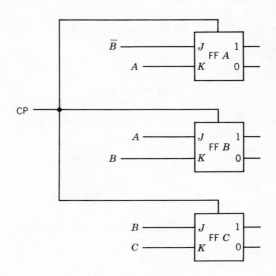

8

FLIP-FLOP PROGRAMMING

Flip-flops (FFs) are the prime memory element in digital circuits. In the days of discrete circuits flip-flops were composed of two transistor (or vacuum-tube) amplifiers cross-coupled in such a way that when one was on the other was off. The monolithic integrated-circuit flip-flop is a much more sophisticated and elegant device, being composed of many diodes and transistors, and is totally contained in one TO-5 transistor can or integrated-circuit flat pack. The free use of active components in monolithic-chip, integrated circuits has resulted in flip-flop designs that are easily programmed with a minimum of external logic and have good fan-out capability and very high frequency characteristics.

There are essentially four basic types of flip-flops—the D, T, $S\text{-}R$, and $J\text{-}K$—as defined by their individual characteristic tables and excitation tables. The characteristic table is used in analyzing FFs, whereas the excitation table is used in programming FFs. The characteristic table is the one generally used by the manufacturers of integrated circuits, because it is brief and completely characterizes the operation of the flip-flop. It is explicit and defines the state of the output as a function of the state of the inputs. Each of the FFs discussed is assumed to be a clocked device; that is, the device does not change state until the clock pulse (CP) input has changed state. Q^n refers to the state of the device before the CP occurs, and Q^{n+1} refers to the state of the device after the occurrence of a CP. It should be restated that positive logic is assumed and the FFs will change state (if they are programmed to do so) as a result of the occurrence of a clock pulse.

The techniques described in this chapter can be used with any type of FF, but it may be necessary to develop a new excitation table from the manufacturer's characteristic table because the particular device may respond to negative logic instead of positive logic, and to the falling edge of the CP

165

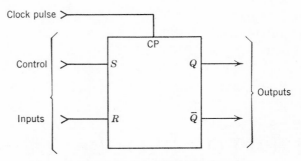

Figure 8.1   Generalized flip-flop.

instead of the rising edge. It may be a d-c–coupled FF, which does not require a CP, or it may be a two-phase FF, which requires a two-phase clock. Obviously the vendor's data sheets must be consulted and carefully analyzed before applying the specific techniques described herein, as well as attempting to utilize a specific FF.

A generalized flip-flop, Q, has a pulse (clock pulse) input, one or more control or steering inputs (such as the S-R inputs), and two outputs known as the normal output, Q, and its complement, $\bar{Q}$, as shown in Figure 8.1. The control or steering inputs determine what the state of the FF will be after a CP has come and gone; thus they "steer" the FF. These are also called the programmed or programmable inputs. The normal or Q output is arbitrary initially but, once defined for a particular programming situation, must not be changed. This simply means that if, for example, pins 6 and 9 are the two outputs from a particular integrated circuit FF and pin 6 is defined as the Q output, then by definition pin 9 is the $\bar{Q}$ or complement output. Conversely there is nothing to prevent defining pin 6 as the $\bar{Q}$ output; all this means is that pin 9 is now the normal or Q output. Care must be taken, however, to define the characteristic and excitation tables to match the definition applied to the FF.

8.1   *D* FLIP-FLOP

The *D*-type FF shown in Figure 8.2 is the simplest type of device from a control point of view. The inputs at the time the CP occurs completely determine the form it will assume. Thus, if a logic 1 is applied to the D input, regardless of what state the FF is in before the pulse it will assume a 1 state on its normal Q output when a pulse has occurred. Similarly, if the D input is a logic 0 when the pulse occurs, it will assume a logic 0 state in its Q output (the $\bar{Q}$ output will of course be the complement, or a logic 1). This is what the characteristic table means. The excitation table means that

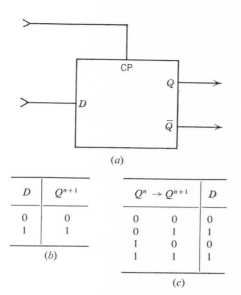

(a)

D	Q^{n+1}
0	0
1	1

(b)

$Q^n \to Q^{n+1}$		D
0	0	0
0	1	1
1	0	0
1	1	1

(c)

Figure 8.2   D-type flip-flop: (a) logic diagram; (b) characteristic table; (c) excitation table.

if the FF is in the 0 state (the normal Q output is a logic 0) and it is required to remain in the 0 state after the occurrence of a CP—that is, $0 \to 0$—then the D input should be programmed with a logic 0. If the FF is in the 1 state and it is desired to have it go to a 0 state—that is, $1 \to 0$—then the D input must be programmed with a logic 0. This can be more simply stated by saying that, regardless of the state of the FF at time n, if it is desired to have the FF go to a 0 state at time $n + 1$ the D input must be logic 0. Likewise, if it is desired to have the FF go to a logic 1 state at time $n + 1$, the D input must be a logic 1 at time n.

This type of FF is useful when transferring data from one source to another. That is, suppose a computer wants to send information to another device and to do so in parallel. The computer will send a control signal telling the device that the information is ready to be received. The device will then generate a clock pulse that strobes the FFs, and they will assume the state of the input data lines. The device then signals the computer that it has received the data and the transfer is complete.

8.2   T FLIP-FLOP

The T flip-flop shown in Figure 8.3 gets its name from the ability to toggle or change state with every input clock pulse as long as the control input T is at logic 1. That is, regardless of the state of the FF at time n, it will assume

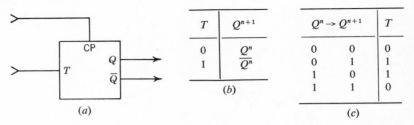

T	Q^{n+1}
0	Q^n
1	$\overline{Q^n}$

(b)

$Q^n \to Q^{n+1}$		T
0	0	0
0	1	1
1	0	1
1	1	0

(c)

(a)

Figure 8.3 *T*-type flip-flop: (*a*) logic diagram; (*b*) characteristic table; (*c*) excitation table.

the complement state on command of a pulse if the input T is high. This is what is meant in the characteristic table by the $\overline{Q^n}$; whatever it was at time n it will be the complement of this at time $n + 1$. The excitation table for this device is also simple. Any time it is desired to have the FF change state it is only required to program the T input with logic 1. Whenever it is desired that the FF remain stable and not change state, the T input must be held to logic 0. This is illustrated by the timing diagram of Figure 8.3*a*. It will be seen that although this type of FF is not generally available the characteristics of this device are included in other types, so that the toggling feature is a normal programming consideration. For example, because a T flip-flop will change state every time a pulse is applied and the input is a logic 1, it will be in the 1 state for only half the input pulses, thus acting as a divider or a count-down device. A single T flip-flop is therefore a divide-by-2 device. This would be the same as the least significant bit in a binary truth table, where the least significant bit changes state with every input count.

8.3 *S-R* FLIP-FLOP

The *S-R* or set-reset flip-flop can be programmed or steered to any desired state by programming the inputs, as defined in Figure 8.4. This type of FF is the one most commonly built from discrete circuits and is still furnished by a large number of IC manufacturers. It is easy to program and simple to understand. The device characterized here remains stable as long as the S and R inputs are in the logic 0 state. If S is raised to 1 the FF assumes a 1 state on its output, whereas if R is raised to 1 the FF assumes a logic 0 on its output. The one shortcoming of this device is that care must be taken to be sure both inputs are not in the logic 1 state at the same time. This is like trying to turn on both output transistors at the same time when only one wants to be on. In fact, this is exactly what can happen in some *S-R* flip-flops. This is what is meant by the question mark for the Q^{n+1} state when both

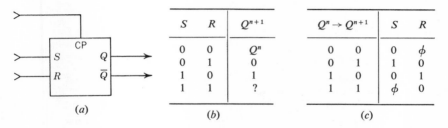

	S	R	Q^{n+1}		$Q^n \to Q^{n+1}$		S	R
	0	0	Q^n		0	0	0	ϕ
	0	1	0		0	1	1	0
	1	0	1		1	0	0	1
	1	1	?		1	1	ϕ	0
(a)		(b)				(c)		

Figure 8.4 S-R-type flip-flop: (a) logic diagram; (b) characteristic table; (c) excitation table.

inputs are high in the characteristic table. The output is indeterminate—is unknown—and there is no way to predict what state the output will be in when both inputs are high and a pulse occurs. Therefore this is called a forbidden state and is to be avoided by appropriate programming of the inputs S and R.

The excitation table for this FF contains the symbol ϕ. This symbol represents a "don't care" condition; that is, it makes no difference whether the input is a 1 or a 0. The excitation table is generally developed from the characteristic table by deductive analysis, as it is furnished with the data sheets. That is, if the FF is in the 0 state at time n and it is desired to have it remain in the 0 state after the occurrence of a pulse or at time $n + 1$, then from the characteristic table it can be seen that if the S and R inputs are both 0 then the FF will not change state. Therefore S should be 0 and R should be 0. However, since it is desired to have the FF in the 0 state at time $n + 1$ it really doesn't matter if R just happens to be 1 when the pulse occurs. Thus R can be 1 or 0 and the FF will still assume a 0 state at time $n + 1$. Therefore the entry under S and R for the condition that Q^n is 0 and Q^{n+1} is also 0 is for $S = 0$ and $R = \phi$.

If the FF is in the 0 state and it is desired to have it go to the 1 state—that is, $0 \to 1$ under Q^n and Q^{n+1}—then from the characteristic table, for the FF to be in the 1 state at time $n + 1$, the only satisfactory condition is $S = 1$ and $R = 0$. Therefore the entry for the $0 \to 1$ state is for S-R to be 1-0.

If the FF is in the 1 state and it is desired to have it go to the 0 state, then $S = 0$ and $R = 1$ from the characteristic table. The final condition that can occur is for the FF to be in the 1 state and remain in the 1 state, or $1 \to 1$ under the Q^n and Q^{n+1} headings. If the FF is required to be in the 1 state certainly R must remain in the logic 0 state. However, S may be 1 or 0 because a 1 state is desired at $n + 1$. Therefore the correct entry under S-R is ϕ-0.

8.4   *J-K* FLIP-FLOP

The *J-K* flip-flop can be considered a refinement of the *S-R* FF in that the indeterminate state of the *S-R* type is defined in the *J-K* type. Figure 8.5 illustrates the *J-K* along with its characteristic and excitation tables. The characteristic table for the *J-K* FF is different in that if both *J* and *K* inputs are high the FF will change state. That is, if the control inputs are high and the FF is in the 0 state it will change to a 1 state when a pulse occurs. Conversely, if it is in the 1 state and both *J* and *K* are high when the pulse occurs, the FF will change to the 0 state. This is characteristic of the *T* FF. The *J-K* FF therefore has the features of both an *S-R* device and a *T* device.

The *J-K* FF was not often used in discrete circuit design because it took many transistors and components to implement the circuit. Integrated circuits, on the other hand, can achieve many transistors and diodes on a single chip without increasing chip cost. Therefore almost all integrated-circuit logic families include one or more *J-K* devices.

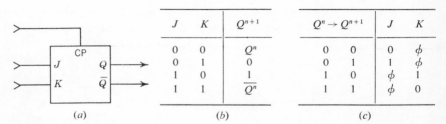

		J	K	Q^{n+1}		$Q^n \rightarrow Q^{n+1}$		J	K
		0	0	Q^n		0	0	0	ϕ
		0	1	0		0	1	1	ϕ
		1	0	1		1	0	ϕ	1
		1	1	$\overline{Q^n}$		1	1	ϕ	0
(*a*)			(*b*)			(*c*)			

Figure 8.5   *J-K*–type flip-flop: (*a*) logic diagram; (*b*) characteristic table; (*c*) excitation table.

The excitation table for the *J-K* FF in Figure 8.5*c* further illustrates the versatility of this device by the generous number of ϕ terms. These ϕ terms indicate that the logic level input can be either 0 or 1 and thus can result in minimum logic programming. This will become evident in the next chapter.

8.5 FLIP-FLOP PROGRAMMING

The design of pulse sequential networks requires the programming or sequencing of FFs through some required sequence. This requires a knowledge of sequential networks as well as combinational networks, for it is the combinational network that provides the logic function required for the control inputs. In the case of three *S-R* flip-flops there is an *S* input and an *R* input for each of the three flip-flops, and each input must be controlled.

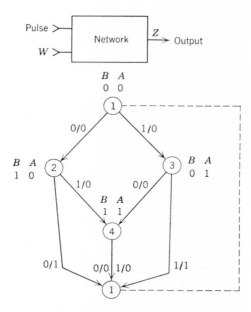

Figure 8.6 State diagram.

Each input is usually dependent, not only on the state of inputs to the network, but also on the state of each memory element or FF within the network. This requires the solution of multifunctional combinational networks. The state diagram in Figure 8.6 will be used to illustrate the point.

EXAMPLE 8.1. *Given the state diagram with secondary assignments as shown in Figure 8.6, design the combinational network necessary for the sequence shown using S-R type flip-flops.*

The first step is to create a transition table. This table defines the present state of each FF and the desired next state as a result of various states of the input. This is shown in Figure 8.7a. The excitation table for an S-R flip-flop is repeated in Figure 8.7b for ready reference. A separate control matrix is required for each FF. One FF is labeled A and the other is labeled B. The S input of FF A is identified as S_A, and the S input to FF B is identified as S_B. The R control input to each FF is also identified by subscripts A and B.

Three things determine the sequence of the network: the logic level of the input, W, and the state of FFs A and B. Thus if the network is in state 1 FF A is 0 and FF B is 0. If when the pulse occurs, W is 0, the network is to be programmed so that A remains 0 while B goes to 1. Therefore in the control matrix for S_A and R_A the entry for S_A-R_A in the $A = B = W = 0$ cell is for FF A to remain 0. Referring to the excitation table for an S-R FF,

Present state			Next state	
	FF		Input—W	
State	B	A	0	1
1	0	0	1 0	0 1
2	1	0	0 0	1 1
3	0	1	1 1	0 0
4	1	1	0 0	0 0

(a)

$Q^n \to Q^{n+1}$		S	R
0	0	0	ϕ
0	1	1	0
1	0	0	1
1	1	ϕ	0

(b)

A \ W	0	1
00	0 ϕ	1 0
01	ϕ 0	0 1
11	0 1	0 1
10	0 ϕ	1 0

S_A—R_A

A \ W	0	1
00	1 0	0 ϕ
01	1 0	0 ϕ
11	0 1	0 1
10	0 1	ϕ 0

S_B—R_B

(c)

Figure 8.7 (a) Transition table; (b) excitation table; (c) control matrices.

the S and R control inputs should be 0 for S and ϕ for R. The control matrix is completed in this fashion. Each cell is examined to determine the requirements on the control inputs for each combination of conditions that can occur. For example, the S_B-R_B entry in the cell for FF $A = 1$ and FF $B = 1$ is 0-1 because the two FFs are required to go to 0 for the conditions of $W = 0$ as well as $W = 1$. The ϕ conditions are useful in minimizing the required control network for S_A, R_A, S_B, and R_B.

Analysis of the control matrix in Figure 8.7c yields the following equations for S_A, R_A, S_B and R_B:

$$S_A = \bar{A}W$$
$$R_A = AW + AB$$
$$S_B = \bar{B}\,\bar{W}$$
$$R_B = B\bar{W} + AB \quad (\text{or } B\bar{W} + AW).$$

This results in the network shown in Figure 8.8. The output is desired from state 2 with $W = 0$ or from state 3 with $W = 1$. Therefore $Z = \bar{A}B\bar{W} + A\bar{B}W$.

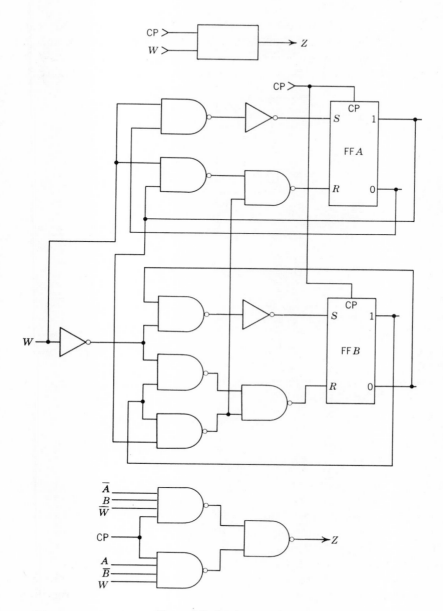

Figure 8.8 Logic network.

Variations in the network can be achieved by changing the secondary assignments or selecting a different type of FF to implement the function. Figures 8.9 and 8.10 show the same problem implemented with a J-K flip-flop. The excitation table for the J-K flip-flop is repeated in Figure 8.9a,

$Q^n \rightarrow Q^{n+1}$		J	K
0	0	0	ϕ
0	1	1	ϕ
1	0	ϕ	1
1	1	ϕ	0

(a)

$\begin{matrix}B & W\\A\end{matrix}$	0	1
00	0 ϕ	1 ϕ
01	ϕ 0	ϕ 1
11	ϕ 1	ϕ 1
10	0 ϕ	1 ϕ

J_A-K_A

$\begin{matrix}B & W\\A\end{matrix}$	0	1
00	1 ϕ	0 ϕ
01	1 ϕ	0 ϕ
11	ϕ 1	ϕ 1
10	ϕ 1	ϕ 0

J_B-K_B

(b)

$$J_A = W$$
$$K_A = W + B$$
$$J_B = \overline{W}$$
$$K_B = \overline{W} + A$$

(c)

Figure 8.9 (a) J-K excitation table; (b) control matrices; (c) control equations.

and the control matrix is shown in Figure 8.9b. This control matrix is developed from the transition table in Figure 8.7a and the J-K excitation table. In state 2, where $B = 1$ and $A = 0$, if $W = 0$ it is required that B go from 1 to 0. Thus the J-K entry in the J_B-K_B control matrix in the $A = 0$, $B = 1$, $W = 0$ cell is $\phi 1$. In the cell where $A = 1$, $B = 0$, and $W = 1$ (state 3 and $W = 1$) the transition for A is from 1 to 0, whereas for B the transition is from 0 to 0.

The equations in Figure 8.9c are a result of the control matrices and illustrate the dramatic change in implementation as a result of using the J-K instead of the S-R flip-flop. Figure 8.10 shows the completed network. The

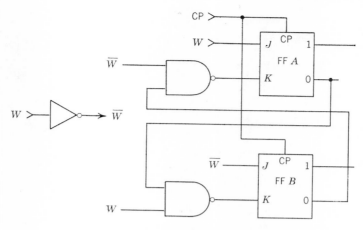

Figure 8.10 *J-K* flip-flops.

output is independent of the type of flip-flop, and depends only on the state conditions. Therefore the output network must be the same as shown in Figure 8.8.

The previous example illustrates the basic techniques required to implement pulse sequential networks. The development of a state diagram is independent of the type of FF used; however, the secondary assignment can be influenced by the FF selected. The synthesizing of pulse sequential networks, therefore, requires the following procedural steps:

1. Create primitive state diagram.
2. Fill in primitive state table.
3. Remove redundant states.
4. Create final state table and state diagram.
5. Select FF type (if not already predetermined by logic family selection).
6. Make secondary assignment.
7. Create a transition table.
8. With the aid of the FF excitation table and the program transition table, develop required control matrices for the control inputs of each FF.
9. Apply combinational network techniques to evolve minimal networks for individual control of the FFs.

Some more examples will assist in clarifying these procedures.

EXAMPLE 8.2. Example 7.1 resulted in a state diagram (Fig. 7.5) and a suggested secondary assignment (Fig. 7.10a) for a network that would produce an output if an odd number of 1's occurred in three successive data bits. The transition table for this assignment appears in Figure 8.11,

Present state				Next state	
				Input	
State	A	B	C	0	1
1	0	0	0	010	001
2	0	0	1	100	011
3	0	1	0	011	100
4	0	1	1	000	000
5	1	0	0	000	000

(a)

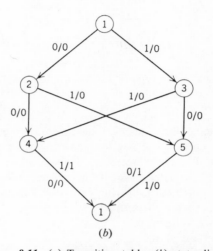

(b)

Figure 8.11 (a) Transition table; (b) state diagram.

with the secondary assignment assumed in Figure 7.10b. A *J-K* type of FF will be assumed available for this example. At this point the step is to use the *J-K* excitation table and the required transitions to develop the control matrix for each FF. The problem requires three FFs; therefore a separate control matrix, containing a listing of the state of the control inputs for each transition, is developed for each FF. Figure 8.12 shows the *J-K* excitation table and the three control matrices. Inspection of the transition table and excitation table show that if the network is in state 1, where $A = B = C = 0$, and if $W = 0$, the program must be such that FF *A* remains 0, *B* goes to 1, and *C* remains 0. Then, in the 0000 cell of the control matrix for FF *A*, the J_A-K_A entry is 0ϕ. That is, *A* goes from 0 to 0. FF *B* is 0 and should be programmed to go to 1 when in state 1 and $W = 0$; therefore the entry in the 0000 cell for J_B-K_B is 1ϕ. This step-by-step programming is continued for

$Q^n \to Q^{n+1}$		J	K
0	0	0	ϕ
0	1	1	ϕ
1	0	ϕ	1
1	1	ϕ	0

(a)

A \ C B	W 0 0	0 1	1 1	1 0
00	0 ϕ	0 ϕ	0 ϕ	1 ϕ
01	0 ϕ	1 ϕ	0 ϕ	0 ϕ
11	—	—	—	—
10	ϕ 1	ϕ 1	—	—

$J_A\text{-}K_A$
(b)

A \ C B	W 0 0	0 1	1 1	1 0
00	1 ϕ	0 ϕ	1 ϕ	0 ϕ
01	ϕ 0	ϕ 1	ϕ 1	ϕ 1
11	—	—	—	—
10	0 ϕ	0 ϕ	—	—

$J_B\text{-}K_B$
(c)

A \ C B	W 0 0	0 1	1 1	1 0
00	0 ϕ	1 ϕ	ϕ 0	ϕ 1
01	1 ϕ	0 ϕ	ϕ 1	ϕ 1
11	—	—	—	—
10	0 ϕ	0 ϕ	—	—

$J_C\text{-}K_C$
(d)

Figure 8.12 (a) J-K excitation table; (b–d) control matrices.

177

each combinational entry of W and each state assignment. There are three states of FFs that are not defined, which, along with the two possible states of W, provide six undefined cells in the control matrices of Figure 8.12. For the purposes of this example it will be assumed that these cells are "don't care" conditions. That is, these particular combinations will not occur or, if they do, it will not matter. At any rate these cells can be used to minimize the control equations and resultant network. Figure 8.13 reproduces the three control matrices with the unused cells designated as all ϕ's and the

FF A: $J_A = \bar{B}C\bar{W} + B\bar{C}W$
$\quad\quad K_A = A$

$A\backslash C$ B $\quad W$	00	01	11	10
00	0 ϕ	0 ϕ	0 ϕ	1 ϕ
01	0 ϕ	1 ϕ	0 ϕ	0 ϕ
11	ϕ ϕ	ϕ ϕ	ϕ ϕ	ϕ ϕ
10	ϕ 1	ϕ 1	ϕ ϕ	ϕ ϕ

$$J_A\text{-}K_A$$

FF B: $J_B = \bar{A}\bar{C}\bar{W} + CW$
$\quad\quad K_B = C + W$

$A\backslash C$ B $\quad W$	00	01	11	10
00	1 ϕ	0 ϕ	ϕ 1	ϕ 1
01	ϕ 0	ϕ 1	ϕ 1	ϕ 1
11	ϕ ϕ	ϕ ϕ	ϕ ϕ	ϕ ϕ
10	0 ϕ	0 ϕ	ϕ ϕ	ϕ ϕ

$$J_B\text{-}K_B$$

FF C: $J_C = B + \bar{W}\bar{A}\bar{B}W$
$\quad\quad K_C = B + \bar{W}$

$A\backslash C$ B $\quad W$	00	01	11	10
00	0 ϕ	1 ϕ	ϕ 0	ϕ 1
01	1 ϕ	0 ϕ	ϕ 1	ϕ 1
11	ϕ ϕ	ϕ ϕ	ϕ ϕ	ϕ ϕ
10	0 ϕ	0 ϕ	ϕ ϕ	ϕ ϕ

$$J_C\text{-}K_C$$

Figure 8.13   Control equations.

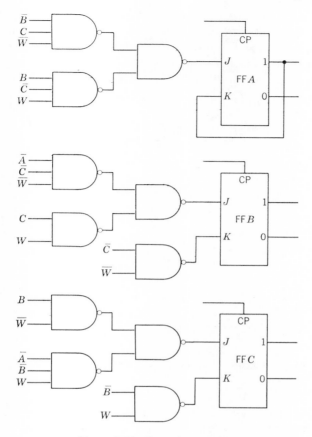

Figure 8.14   Control networks.

resulting equations alongside. These may be the minimal equations for each function but do not necessarily result in the minimal network. It is left to the student to develop combinational networks requiring fewer gates than those shown in Figure 8.14.

Referring to the state diagram in Figure 8.11, an output is required for state 4 if $W = 1$ and for state 5 if $W = 0$. Figure 8.15 shows the development of the output function. An output matrix is drawn showing the states and input conditions for an output. In addition, the states that do not occur can be treated as ϕ or "don't-care" states and are used to minimize the implementation of the output. The output matrix in Figure 8.15a results in the equation shown, and the final part of the problem is the output network shown in Figure 8.15c.

$A \backslash C$ $B \quad W$	00	01	11	10
00	0	0	0	0
01	0	0	1	0
11	0	0	0	0
10	1	0	0	0

$$Z$$
$$(a)$$

$$Z = A\overline{W} + BCW$$
$$(b)$$

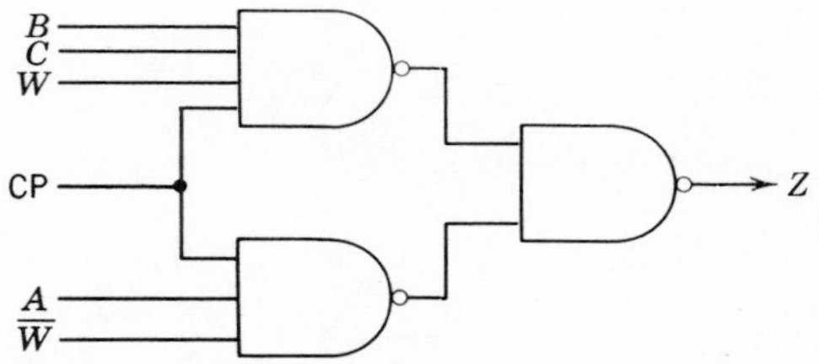

$$(c)$$

Figure 8.15 Output function—Example 8.2: (a) output matrix; (b) output equation; (c) output network.

The output of the pulse sequential network shown here is a pulse. That is, the CP is the output when the proper conditions have been satisfied as required by the sequential network. Another variation to this would be when the output is a given state assignment of the FFs. This is the case when the FFs are programmed as a counter and a particular count or state of the FFs is the required output. This will be illustrated in Chapter 9.

EXAMPLE 8.3. The second example of Chapter 7 was for a network that would produce an output if the input sequence was a decimal 6 or 8 in BCD code. The required state diagram and state table are reproduced in Figure 8.16. A T-type FF will be assumed for this example. The assumed secondary assignment, with resultant next states, is shown in the transition table of Figure 8.17a. The excitation table for the T flip-flop is also shown for reference purposes. The next step is to create the control matrices for the three flip-flops, as shown in Figure 8.18. This time there is only one control input for each FF; thus there is only one entry in each control matrix. Also, eight states are required, and this does not leave any unassigned states. The transition from state 1, with $W = 0$, is to state 2. Thus the only FF that

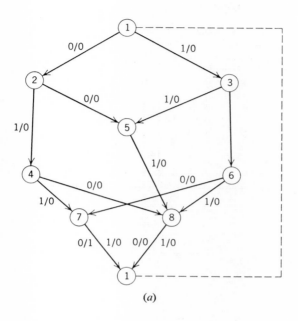

(a)

Present state				Next state		Output	
	Assignment			Input		Input	
State	A	B	C	0	1	0	1
1	0	0	0	2	3	0	0
2	0	0	1	5	4	0	0
3	0	1	0	6	5	0	0
4	0	1	1	8	7	0	0
5	1	0	0	8	8	0	0
6	1	0	1	7	8	0	0
7	1	1	0	1	1	1	0
8	1	1	1	1	1	0	0

(b)

Figure 8.16 (a) State diagram; (b) state table.

Present state				Next state					
Assignment				Input					
State	A	B	C	0			1		
1	0	0	0	0	0	1	0	1	0
2	0	0	1	1	0	0	0	1	1
3	0	1	0	1	0	1	1	0	0
4	0	1	1	1	1	1	1	1	0
5	1	0	0	1	1	1	1	1	1
6	1	0	1	1	1	0	1	1	1
7	1	1	0	0	0	0	0	0	0
8	1	1	1	0	0	0	0	0	0

(a)

$Q^n \rightarrow Q^{n+1}$		T
0	0	0
0	1	1
1	0	1
1	1	0

(b)

Figure 8.17 T-type flip-flop: (a) transition table; (b) excitation table.

changes state is the C FF. The entry in the 0000 cell of the control FFs is 0 for T_A and T_B and 1 for T_C. The transitions from state 7 are to state 1 for both $W = 0$ and $W = 1$. Therefore entries in the cells for 1100 (state 7 with $W = 0$) and 1101 cell (state 7 with $W = 1$) are for A to change state, B to change state, and C to remain stable. This programming continues until each cell of each map is filled. An equation representative of the entries in the various matrices is then written.

The secondary assignment chosen for the example was a straight binary count representing each state. This choice in secondary assignments and the selection of the T FF have resulted in the control equations of Figure 8.18 and the implementation shown in Figure 8.19. This is just one of the many networks possible. A much simpler (or more complex) network could result from a different secondary assignment and/or FF selection. It should be noted, however, that all possible alternatives cannot be tried because of the time and expense involved. If a circuit is to be used only once in a system the first design is usually justified solely on the basis that the cost in engineering time to eliminate a few logic gates is far greater than the cost

FF A: $T_A = B + \bar{A}C\bar{W}$

$\begin{array}{c}A \backslash C \\ B\end{array}$

W	00	01	11	10
00	0	0	0	1
01	1	1	1	1
11	1	1	1	1
10	0	0	0	0

T_A

FF B: $T_B = \bar{B}W + B\bar{W} + A$

$\begin{array}{c}A \backslash C \\ B\end{array}$

W	00	01	11	10
00	0	1	1	0
01	1	1	0	0
11	1	1	1	1
10	1	1	1	1

T_B

FF C: $T_C = BCW + AC\bar{W} + A\bar{B}\bar{C} + \bar{A}\bar{C}\bar{W} + \bar{A}\bar{B}\bar{W}$

$\begin{array}{c}A \backslash C \\ B\end{array}$

W	00	01	11	10
00	1	0	0	1
01	1	0	1	0
11	0	0	1	1
10	1	1	0	1

T_C

Figure 8.18 Control matrices and control equations.

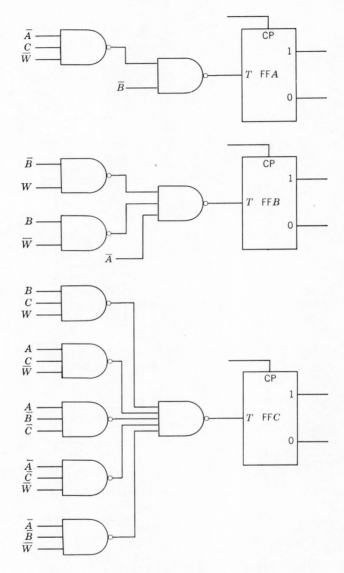

Figure 8.19 Network.

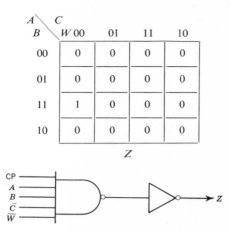

Figure 8.20   Output matrix and network.

of the gates eliminated. Figure 8.20 shows the output matrix and resulting output network for the output Z.

8.6 NEW ANALYSIS TECHNIQUE

The preceding analysis in Chapter 7 of the network in Figure 7.1 seems clumsy and tedious. An approach that simplifies the analysis of a pulsed sequential network will now be illustrated with the use of the network in Figure 7.1. The first step is the same as before, to write the equations for the control inputs to each FF. These equations are repeated in Figure 8.21a. There are

four variables involved: A, B, C, and the input W; thus a 4-bit program matrix is required for each of the three FFs. The entries in the program matrix are the result of the excitation equations for each FF. The S_A and R_A equations are used to fill the S_A-R_A program matrix, where the first entry in each cell is the result of the S_A equation and the second entry is the result of the R_A equation. Thus the cells where $\bar{B}$ and C are 1 as well as where $\bar{B}$ and $\bar{W}$ are 1 must contain a 1 for the S_A entry. R_A is 1 whenever B is 1. The plotting of these excitation equations results in the program matrices shown. These program matrices are used, along with the characteristic table, to produce the state matrices shown in Figure 8.22. The first cell in the S_A-R_A program matrix is a 1-0 entry. The characteristic table defines the next state of an S-R FF as 1 when the input controls are programmed with 1-0. Therefore in the first cell of the A-state matrix the entry is 1. Every cell that contains a 1-0 entry indicates that the FF is programmed to go to 1 when a pulse occurs. Any cell that contains the input

$$S_A = \bar{B}C + \bar{B}\overline{W}$$

$$R_A = B$$

$$S_B = A\bar{B} + \bar{B}C$$

$$R_B = B$$

$$S_C = \bar{A}W$$

$$R_C = B + \overline{W}$$

(a)

W\B C\A	00	01	11	10
00	10	10	01	01
01	10	10	01	01
01	10	10	01	01
10	00	00	01	01

S_A-R_A

W\B C\A	00	01	11	10
00	00	10	01	01
01	10	10	01	01
11	10	10	01	01
10	00	10	01	01

S_B-R_B

W\B C\A	00	01	11	10
00	01	01	01	01
01	01	01	01	01
11	10	00	01	11
10	10	00	01	11

S_C-R_C

(b)

Figure 8.21 New analysis of Example 7.1: (a) excitation equations; (b) program matrices.

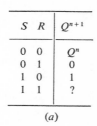

$$\begin{array}{cc|c} S & R & Q^{n+1} \\ \hline 0 & 0 & Q^n \\ 0 & 1 & 0 \\ 1 & 0 & 1 \\ 1 & 1 & ? \end{array}$$

(a)

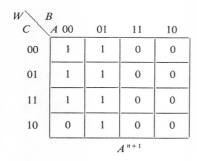

A^{n+1}

B^{n+1}

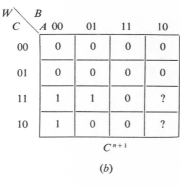

C^{n+1}

(b)

$$Z = (BCW)CP$$

(c)

Figure 8.22 Analysis of Example 7.1: (a) S-R characteristic table; (b) state matrices A, B, and C; (c) output equation.

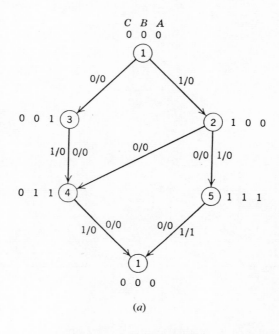

(a)

From					Next state		
W	C	B	A		C	B	A
0	0	1	0	→	0	0	0
1	0	1	0	→	?	0	0
0	1	0	1	→	0	1	1
1	1	0	1	→	1	1	1
0	1	1	0	→	0	0	0
1	1	1	0	→	?	0	0

(b)

Figure 8.23 Analysis of Example 7.1: complete state diagram.

188

program 0-1 defines the next state of the FF as 0. Thus a 0 is placed in the corresponding cells of the state matrix.

The program matrix is a mapping of the excitation states of the inputs to each of the FFs as a function of their present state . The state matrix is a mapping of the next state for each FF. Each cell of the matrix defines a particular state, and the entries in the cells of the program matrix define the excitation whereas the entries in the state matrix define the next state. That is, when $A = 1$, $B = 1$, $C = 0$, and $W = 0$, defining the 0011 cell, the entries are 000 in the respective A, B, and C-state matrices. This indicates that from the 011 state, with $W = 0$, the next state will be the 000 state.

Thus the state diagram shown before in Figure 7.2 and repeated in Figure 8.23 can be completed with ease by referring to the state matrices. In addition the next state for all possible combinations of inputs is available at a glance and can be accounted for as shown.

This procedure is extremely useful in analyzing counters and special-purpose FF programs, as well for checking on the synthesis of a FF program. Experience with this procedure can be gained by applying the technique to the counters implemented in the next chapter.

PROBLEMS

1. The characteristic table for the Signetics S-R flip-flop SE124 is given below. Evolve the excitation table.

S	R	Q^{n+1}
0	0	?
0	1	1
1	0	0
1	1	Q^n

2. Make secondary assignments and design a network for the state diagram shown in Figure 7.13, Example 7.3, of the text.

9

FLIP-FLOP COUNTERS

Flip-flops programmed as counters in one mode or another are found in almost all equipment containing digital logic. A computer continuously counts clock pulses, representing time, to control the sequencing of the internal program. A radar system counts clock pulses, representing elements of time, in order to determine the range of a target. A decoding network may count pulses that determine the step-by-step operation of a programmed sequence of events. There are binary counters, binary-coded decimal (decade or BCD) counters, random counters, synchronous counters, ripple counters, ring counters, and shift registers, to mention a few. This chapter will treat the most important types of counter and give examples of how they are implemented.

9.1 SYNCHRONOUS BINARY COUNTERS

The synchronous binary counter is developed from pulsed sequential network synthesis techniques. A state diagram and state table are drawn defining the required sequence of events followed by development of the FF control matrices and individual FF control networks. A synchronous counter, by definition, is one in which any change in states of the FF's is done on command of a CP and all FF's change state at the same time. Figure 9.1 shows the state diagram and state table for a 4-bit binary counter. The state designations are given a secondary assignment of the binary value of the decimal number. The state of the FFs, at any given point in time, is represented by a binary number that is the binary equivalent of the decimal number. It should be obvious that reference to a 4-bit counter implies four FFs and thus a count of 16. The FFs are identified as A, B, C, and D, with A referred to as the LSB (least significant bit) and flip-flop D given the assignment of MSB (most significant bit). That is, flip-flop A has a decimal weight of $2^0 = 1$, flip-flop B has a weight assignment of $2^1 = 2$, flip-flop C has a weight assignment of $2^2 = 4$, and flip-flop D has a weight of $2^3 = 8$. Therefore state 5 is represented by $A = 1$, $B = 0$, $C = 1$, $D = 0$, which is the binary number 0101.

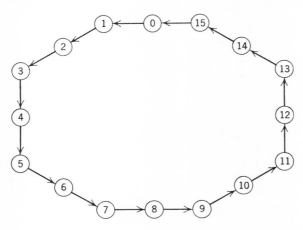

Present state					Next state				
State	D	C	B	A	State	D	C	B	A
0	0	0	0	0	1	0	0	0	1
1	0	0	0	1	2	0	0	1	0
2	0	0	1	0	3	0	0	1	1
3	0	0	1	1	4	0	1	0	0
4	0	1	0	0	5	0	1	0	1
5	0	1	0	1	6	0	1	1	0
6	0	1	1	0	7	0	1	1	1
7	0	1	1	1	8	1	0	0	0
8	1	0	0	0	9	1	0	0	1
9	1	0	0	1	10	1	0	1	0
10	1	0	1	0	11	1	0	1	1
11	1	0	1	1	12	1	1	0	0
12	1	1	0	0	13	1	1	0	1
13	1	1	0	1	14	1	1	1	0
14	1	1	1	0	15	1	1	1	1
15	1	1	1	1	0	0	0	0	0

(*b*)

Figure 9.1 Four-bit synchronous binary counter: (*a*) state diagram; (*b*) state table.

$Q^n \to Q^{n+1}$	J	K
$0 \to 0$	0	ϕ
$0 \to 1$	1	ϕ
$1 \to 0$	ϕ	1
$1 \to 1$	ϕ	0

(a)

C \ A	00	01	11	10
00	0	1	3	2
01	4	5	7	6
11	12	13	15	14
10	8	9	11	10

$D \backslash B$

(b)

C \ A	00	01	11	10
00	1ϕ	$\phi 1$	$\phi 1$	1ϕ
01	1ϕ	$\phi 1$	$\phi 1$	1ϕ
11	1ϕ	$\phi 1$	$\phi 1$	1ϕ
10	1ϕ	$\phi 1$	$\phi 1$	1ϕ

$D \backslash B$

$J_A\text{-}K_A$
$J_A = K_A = 1$
(c)

C \ A	00	01	11	10
00	0ϕ	1ϕ	$\phi 1$	$\phi 0$
01	0ϕ	1ϕ	$\phi 1$	$\phi 0$
11	0ϕ	1ϕ	$\phi 1$	$\phi 0$
10	0ϕ	1ϕ	$\phi 1$	$\phi 0$

$D \backslash B$

$J_B\text{-}K_B$
$J_B = K_B = A$
(d)

C \ A	00	01	11	10
00	0ϕ	0ϕ	1ϕ	0ϕ
01	$\phi 0$	$\phi 0$	$\phi 1$	$\phi 0$
11	$\phi 0$	$\phi 0$	$\phi 1$	$\phi 0$
10	0ϕ	0ϕ	1ϕ	0ϕ

$D \backslash B$

$J_C\text{-}K_C$
$J_C = K_C = AB$
(e)

C \ A	00	01	11	10
00	0ϕ	0ϕ	0ϕ	0ϕ
01	0ϕ	0ϕ	1ϕ	0ϕ
11	$\phi 0$	$\phi 0$	$\phi 1$	$\phi 0$
10	$\phi 0$	$\phi 0$	$\phi 0$	$\phi 0$

$D \backslash B$

$J_D\text{-}K_D$
$J_D = K_D = ABC$
(f)

Figure 9.2 Four-bit synchronous binary counter: (a) excitation table; (b) reference matrix for state assignments; (c–f) control matrices.

192

The programming of four flip-flop to count in a binary sequence next requires the selection of the type of flip-flop. A J-K will be chosen for illustration because it is the most common type of integrated-circuit flip-flop available. The excitation table for a J-K, along with the control matrix and control equations for the four FFs, is shown in Figure 9.2. A reference matrix with the decimal state assignments is also shown to ease the programming problem. The control matrix designated J_A-K_A contains the logic levels required on the J and K control inputs of the A flip-flop at each count or sequential state. An examination of the state table reveals that flip-flop A must change state each time a CP occurs. In state 0, A is 0 but must be programmed to go to 1 when a CP occurs. Thus the entry in the state 0 cell of the J_A-K_A map is a 1ϕ. When in state 1 the A flip-flop must be programmed to go to 0. Thus the entry in the state 1 cell is $\phi 1$. The A flip-flop is required to change state each time, and so it must toggle or act like a T flip-flop with the controls always at logic 1.

The B flip-flop remains at 0 until state 1, at which time it is to go to 1. It remains at 1 for another count before returning to 0. Thus the entry in the state 0 cell of the J_B-K_B map is 0ϕ while the state 1 cell is a 1ϕ. A minimal equation for J_B and K_B is A. This implies that the B FF must change state only when the A FF is 1. An examination of the state table shows this is the case; that is, the B FF must only change from 0 to 1 or from 1 to 0 when the A FF is 1.

The C flip-flop remains a logic 0 until state 4. Thus in state 3 the C FF must be programmed to go from 0 to 1. In state 7 the C FF must be programmed to go from 1 to 0. This condition is satisfied by sensing when FF A and FF B are in the 1 state as implied by the control matrix for the J_C and K_C controls.

The D flip-flop remains 0 until state 8. Therefore entries in cells for states 0 through 6 are for the FF to remain 0. In state 7 the C FF is programmed to go from 0 to 1. It remains 1 until state 15, when it must be programmed to return to 0. The change in state of the C FF occurs only when the lesser-order flip-flops are in the logic 1 state.

Figure 9.3 shows the four flip-flops with appropriate logic on the control inputs to produce the required sequence. The output from this type of network is the state of the flip-flops. Notice that the arrangement of the FFs is such that the signal flow is from left to right, which is the conventional way of laying out a logic diagram. The LSB then is to the left whereas the MSB is to the right. The most significant bit in a binary counter is either the bit with the largest equivalent decimal weight or the bit that changes state the least number of times.

It was recognized in this 4-bit synchronous binary counter that the change in state of each bit (FF) depended on the preceding least significant

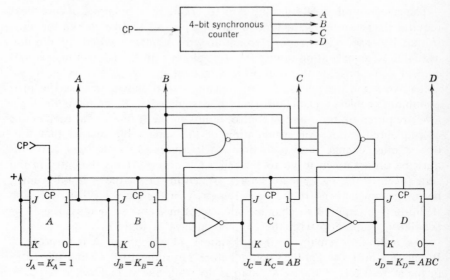

Figure 9.3 Four-bit synchronous counter.

bits. Recognizing this pattern will enable one to extend this programming concept to synchronous binary counters of any length. Figure 9.4 shows seven flip-flops programmed to count in a binary sequence. All J and K inputs are connected in such a way that when the input logic level is 1 the flip-flop will change state. Flip-flop F is programmed to change state whenever all preceding FFs, A, B, C, D, and E, are in the 1 state. Therefore flip-flop F has a decimal weight of $2^5 = 32$ and will change state every time 32 input clock pulses have occurred.

It can be seen that the frequency of operation of this type of counter is limited only by the propagation delay required by a single FF, one NAND gate, and one inverter. That is, because all FFs change state at the same time, the change in state of FF A arrives at the input to the NAND gate controlling FF G at the same time as the change in state of FF E, or D, or any of the other FFs. The change in state of the FFs is said to be transmitted in parallel to each succeeding FF. This requires a continuously increasing fan-in capability on the NAND gates as the length of the counter increases, as well as an increasing fan-out load on the lower-order FFs. The fan-out load on FF A in the 4-bit counter is the J and K inputs to FF B as well as the two NAND gates for C and D, which would be counted as a fan-out load of 4. The fan-out load on FF A in the 7-bit counter is 7. There is a limit on how many leads a given FF can drive, as well as on the fan-in ability of individual NAND gates. When this limit is reached additional line

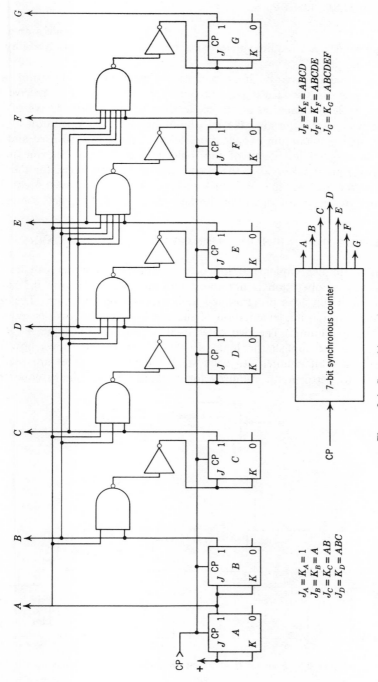

$J_A = K_A = 1$
$J_B = K_B = A$
$J_C = K_C = AB$
$J_D = K_D = ABC$

$J_E = K_E = ABCD$
$J_F = K_F = ABCDE$
$J_G = K_G = ABCDEF$

Figure 9.4 Seven-bit synchronous counter.

195

drivers have to be added to the output of the FFs, and expanders or additional gate logic are required to provide larger equivalent fan-in ability on the NAND gates.

This particular type of implementation—synchronous operation with parallel carry—is the fastest type of binary counter. All FFs receive the change-in-state information at the same time. Propagation delays of one FF and two gates determine the maximum frequency of operation of this counter. If the maximum propagation delay of the FF is 50 nsec and the maximum propagation delay of the logic gate is 20 nsec, the maximum amount of time it takes, after the occurrence of a clock pulse, for the FFs to be programmed for the next clock pulse is $50 + 20 + 20 = 90$ nsec. The maximum frequency of operation is the reciprocal of this, or 11 mHz.

9.2 SYNCHRONOUS BINARY COUNTERS WITH RIPPLE CARRY

A much simpler implementation of a synchronous counter can be had if frequency of operation is not the determining basis. Figure 9.5 shows the same four flip-flops programmed as a synchronous counter. The only difference is in the implementation of the combinational networks required for the programming. The two gates used to perform the logic $A \cdot B$ are also used to accomplish the logic $A \cdot B \cdot C$. Figure 9.6 shows how this extends to a 7-bit counter. In each stage the previous gates are used to advantage to perform the required logic. This type of binary counter is

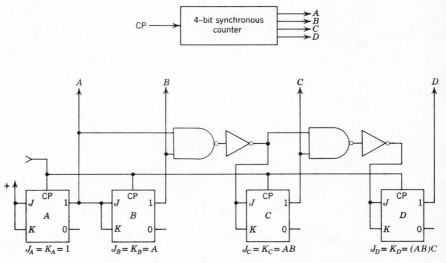

Figure 9.5 Four-bit synchronous counter with ripple carry.

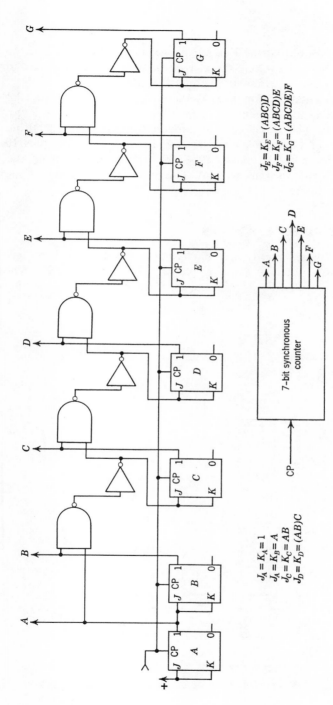

$J_A = K_A = 1$
$J_A = K_B = A$
$J_C = K_C = AB$
$J_D = K_D = (AB)C$

$J_E = K_E = (ABC)D$
$J_F = K_F = (ABCD)E$
$J_G = K_G = (ABCDE)F$

Figure 9.6 Seven-bit synchronous counter with ripple carry.

197

still synchronous in that the FFs all change state at the same time on command of the CP. However, the change in state of FF A must "ripple" through 10 gates in getting to the control inputs of FF G.

This implementation eliminates two basic problems of the parallel carry counter: loading the outputs of the flip-flops, and the need for large fan-in NAND gates. The trade-off is maximum frequency of operation. The 7-bit counter of Figure 9.6 must account for one FF delay plus 10 logic gate delays for a total time of $50 + 200 = 250$ nsec (assuming the same delays used in the previous section). The maximum frequency of this 7-bit counter is therefore 4 mHz.

9.3 BINARY RIPPLE COUNTERS

The third fundamental type of binary counter is illustrated in Figures 9.7 and 9.8 and is referred to as the ripple counter. This is not a synchronous counter, in that all FFs do not change state at the same time; however,

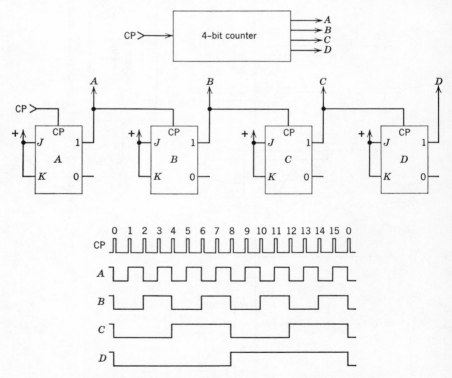

Figure 9.7 Four-bit ripple counter with timing diagram below.

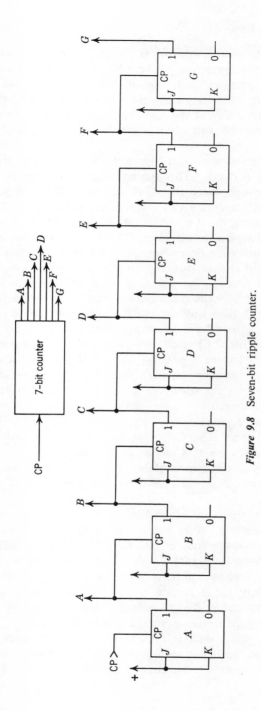

Figure 9.8 Seven-bit ripple counter.

199

the command is still under control of the input CP. An assumption must be made about the operation of the FF. It is assumed that the FF is of the type that operates on the positive-going (rising) edge of the CP. That is, the FF changes state when the CP goes positive and is essentially independent of the width of the CP. This assumption concurs in the type of FF usually designed with discrete circuits and many integrated-circuit flip-flops.

A timing diagram is shown in Figure 9.7 to assist in understanding the operation of this network. This timing diagram represents the sequence of logic states through which the A, B, C, and D flip-flops go in counting from 0 to 15. This concurs with the state diagram in Figure 9.1. As in the synchronous counters, the J and K inputs of the A FF are wired to a logic 1 so that it will change state with each CP. It was previously noted that the B FF should change state only when the A FF was 1. When the input CP causes the A FF to change from 1 to 0 the complement side of the A FF goes from 0 to 1. This change in state of the A FF is used as the CP source for the B FF. That is, because the B FF should change state only when the A goes from 1 to 0, then why not use the complementary $0 \rightarrow 1$ change of the A FF to cause the B FF to change state?

In a like manner the C FF must change only when the B goes from 1 to 0. Therefore the complement of a $0 \rightarrow 1$ change of the B FF can be used to cause the C to change state provided that the flip-flops are wired or programmed to change state whenever a positive-going transition occurs at the CP input. Then each FF is programmed to change state by wiring the J-K inputs to logic 1, and each FF changes state only when the preceding FF goes from 1 to 0. The CP input to Figure 9.7 causes A to change state. The change in state of A causes B to change state. The $1 \rightarrow 0$ transition of B causes C to change state. The $1 \rightarrow 0$ transition of C causes D to change state. Each FF serves as the source for the CP to the next FF.

At state 15 all the FFs are in the 1 state. A CP causes A to change from 1 to 0. This change in A causes B to change, and so on. Thus the information "ripples" down the counter and the FFs essentially change one at a time in rapid sequence. Figure 9.8 illustrates a 7-bit ripple counter. The trade-off with this type of counter is nonsynchronous operation and reduced frequency capability for a minimum logic package count and simplicity of operation. Assuming the 50-nsec flip-flop propagation delay from before, the seven-stage ripple counter in Figure 9.8 has seven delays before the correct data appear on the last FF, for a total delay of $7 \times 50 = 350$ nsec. This type of counter is seldom operated near maximum speed, however, because data normally are desired only when all FFs are stable and not changing state. Ambiguous operation can occur if the frequency of the input CP exceeds the maximum ripple time of the counter. This circuit is used for its economy, not for its speed.

The design of this counter and counters like it is done through intuition and experience. The formal tools of logic design such as those explained in Chapters 6 through 8, serve only as a guide. Reduction in required logic package count is and probably always will be an art.

9.4 BINARY-CODED DECIMAL COUNTERS

A binary-coded decimal counter is an example of a special-purpose counter. It may be nothing more than a 10-state state diagram with a secondary assignment chosen in such a way that the state of the FFs represents the binary equivalent of the decimal number. This is the most common secondary assignment of a BCD counter and has the 8-4-2-1 decimal weight. There must be four FFs involved because there are 10 separate states, which leaves six unassigned states in the total number of possible combinations. Assuming that the FFs are preset to the 0 state, the unassigned states can be treated as ϕ conditions in the control matrix synthesis. Figure 9.9 shows the state diagram and the state table for a BCD counter with the 8-4-2-1 weight. Thus FF D has a decimal weight of 8, C has a weight of 4, B has a weight of 2, and A has a weight of 1. Figure 9.10 shows the resulting control matrix for each FF and the control equations. Inspection of the secondary assignment sequence in the state table and the control matrix equations reveals the intuitive concepts of sequential circuit synthesis. That is, A changes state each CP period. The B FF changes state whenever A is 1 and as long as D is 0. The C FF changes whenever A and B are both 1. The D can be programmed to go to 0 any time A is 1, except when B and C are also 1. When A, B, and C are all 1, the D FF must change state from 0 to 1. This particular synthesis is implemented with appropriate logic gates in Figure 9.11.

Figure 9.12 shows an implementation of the same counter with a ripple-carry feature that reduces the fan-in requirement on the gate controlling J_D from 3 to 2.

This same 8-4-2-1 BCD counter can be synthesized by a divide-by-2 followed by a divide-by-5. The state table in Figure 9.9 shows that the A FF acts as a divide-by-2 device because it changes state each input pulse and thus undergoes a $1 \rightarrow 0$ translation one-half the time. Assuming the same FF as was used in the ripple counter of Figure 9.7, the $0 \rightarrow 1$ transitions of the A FF can be used here as the CP source for the remaining three FFs. This

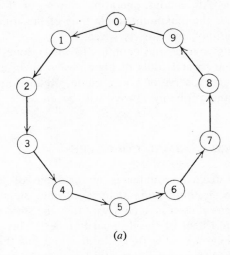

(a)

Present state					Next state				
State	D	C	B	A	State	D	C	B	A
0	0	0	0	0	1	0	0	0	1
1	0	0	0	1	2	0	0	1	0
2	0	0	1	0	3	0	0	1	1
3	0	0	1	1	4	0	1	0	0
4	0	1	0	0	5	0	1	0	1
5	0	1	0	1	6	0	1	1	0
6	0	1	1	0	7	0	1	1	1
7	0	1	1	1	8	1	0	0	0
8	1	0	0	0	9	1	0	0	1
9	1	0	0	1	0	0	0	0	0

(b)

Figure 9.9 BCD counter: (*a*) state diagram; (*b*) state table.

requires the *B*, *C*, and *D* FFs to be programmed as a five-state counter or a divide-by-5 network. The state diagram, secondary assignments, and control matrices for a count-by-5 network are shown in Figure 9.13 and implemented in Figure 9.14. The divide-by-2 *A* FF is then included in Figure 9.15 with the divide-by-5 to form a BCD counter with minimum logic gates. The trade-off is a nonsynchronous counter in which the first FF acts as the CP source for the remaining FFs.

	00	01	11	10
$Q^n \to Q^{n+1}$	**J**	**K**		
0 0	0	φ		
0 1	1	φ		
1 0	φ	1		
1 1	φ	0		

(a)

C\A (D\B)	00	01	11	10
00	0	1	3	2
01	4	5	7	6
11	12	13	15	14
10	8	9	11	10

(b)

C\A (D\B)	00	01	11	10
00	1φ	φ1	φ1	1φ
01	1φ	φ1	φ1	1φ
11	- -	- -	- -	- -
10	1φ	φ1	- -	- -

$J_A\text{-}K_A$
$J_A = K_A = 1$
(c)

C\A (D\B)	00	01	11	10
00	0φ	1φ	φ1	φ0
01	0φ	1φ	φ1	φ0
11	- -	- -	- -	- -
10	0φ	0φ	- -	- -

$J_B\text{-}K_B$
$J_B = K_B = A\bar{D}$
(d)

C\A (D\B)	00	01	11	10
00	0φ	0φ	1φ	φ0
01	φ0	φ0	φ1	φ0
11	- -	- -	- -	- -
10	0φ	0φ	- -	- -

$J_C\text{-}K_C$
$J_C = K_C = AB$
(e)

C\A (D\B)	00	01	11	10
00	0φ	0φ	0φ	0φ
01	0φ	0φ	1φ	0φ
11	- -	- -	- -	- -
10	φ0	φ1	- -	- -

$J_D\text{-}K_D$
$J_D = ABC$
$K_D = A$
(f)

Figure 9.10 BCD synchronous counter: (a) excitation table; (b) reference matrix; (c–f) control matrices.

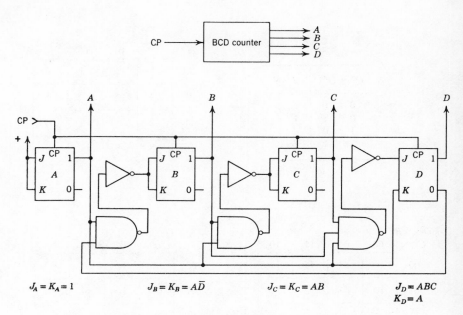

$$J_A = K_A = 1 \qquad J_B = K_B = A\overline{D} \qquad J_C = K_C = AB \qquad J_D = ABC \\ K_D = A$$

Figure 9.11 8-4-2-1 BCD synchronous counter.

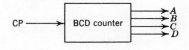

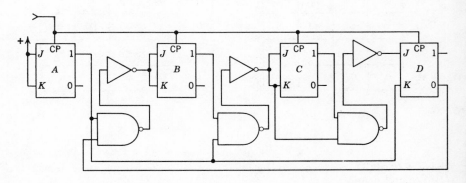

Figure 9.12 8-4-2-1 BCD counter with ripple carry.

204

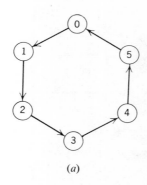

(a)

Present state				Next state			
State	D	C	B	State	D	C	B
0	0	0	0	1	0	0	1
1	0	0	1	2	0	1	0
2	0	1	0	3	0	1	1
3	0	1	1	4	1	0	0
4	1	0	0	0	0	0	0

(b)

C

D \ B	00	01	11	10
0	0	1	3	2
1	4	5	7	6

(c)

C

D \ B	00	01	11	10
0	1ϕ	$\phi1$	1ϕ	1ϕ
1	0ϕ	- -	- -	- -

J_B-K_B
$$J_B = K_B = \bar{D}$$
(d)

C

D \ B	00	01	11	10
0	0ϕ	1ϕ	$\phi1$	$\phi0$
1	0ϕ	- -	- -	- -

J_C-K_C
$$J_C = K_C = B$$
(e)

C

D \ B	00	01	11	10
0	0ϕ	0ϕ	1ϕ	0ϕ
1	$\phi1$	- -	- -	- -

J_D-K_D
$$J_D = BC$$
$$K_D = D$$
(f)

Figure 9.13 Modulo 5 synchronous counter: (*a*) state diagram; (*b*) state table; (*c*) reference matrix; (*d*–*f*) control matrices.

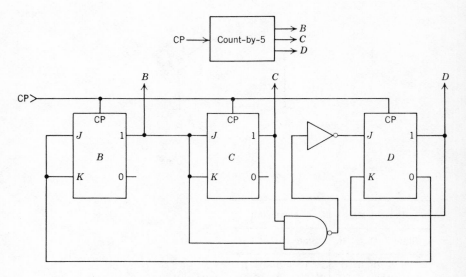

Figure 9.14 Modulo 5 synchronous counter.

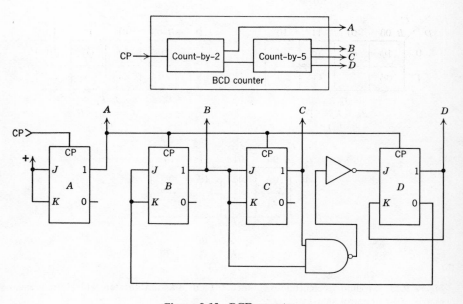

Figure 9.15 BCD counter.

206

9.5 SHIFT REGISTERS

A shift register is a group of FFs programmed in such a way that data shift from one FF to the next in synchrony with a command CP. It generally has a single data line input and shifts from left to right. Figure 9.16

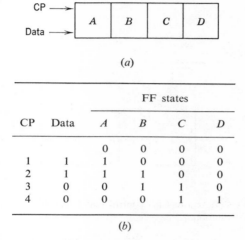

(a)

		FF states			
CP	Data	A	B	C	D
		0	0	0	0
1	1	1	0	0	0
2	1	1	1	0	0
3	0	0	1	1	0
4	0	0	0	1	1

(b)

Figure 9.16 Shift register analysis: (*a*) 4-bit shift register; (*b*) shift register timing chart.

depicts a 4-bit shift register composed of FFs *A*, *B*, *C*, and *D*. The FFs are programmed so that each FF assumes the state of the FF to its left on command of the CP. Thus every time a pulse occurs FF *C* assumes whatever state FF *B* was in, while FF *B* assumes the previous state of FF *A* and FF *A* assumes the state of the data input at the time the pulse occurred. The timing chart in Figure 9.16 shows the result of four consecutive CP periods in which the data were 1100. With the register initially at zero, after four pulses it contains the data 1100, reading from right to left. This particular 4-bit shift register could be used to receive BCD data in serial and, after four CPs, provide the data as parallel outputs from the four FFs. Thus it would be acting as a series-to-parallel converter.

The implementation of a 4-bit shift register is shown in Figure 9.17 with *J-K* FFs. It requires the simplest of programming, in that each FF need only assume the state of the previous FF. Thus if *A* is 1 FF *B* is to go to 1 when a pulse occurs, or if *A* is 0 FF *B* is to go to 0 when a pulse occurs. Figure 9.17a shows the control matrix for the *B* FF.

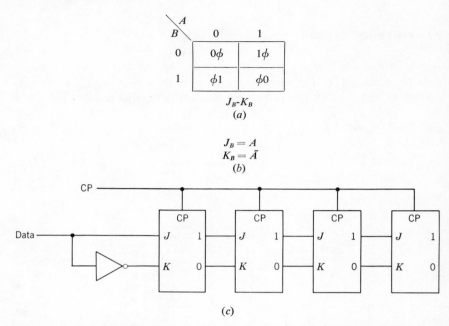

Figure 9.17 Four-bit shift register: (*a*) control matrix for *B* FF; (*b*) control equations for *B* FF; (*c*) implementation.

The *B* FF is dependent only on the state of the *A* FF and its own state. Thus a 2-bit control matrix is all that is required. If the *A* FF is 0, then the *B* FF must go to 0. Thus, if $A = 0$ and $B = 0$, the transition for *B* is from 0 to 0. If *B* is 1 while *A* is 0, the transition is from 1 to 0. Thus entries in the control matrix under $A = 0$ are 0ϕ and $\phi 1$. Under the column for $A = 1$ the transitions are to 1, or $0 \to 1$ and $1 \to 1$ for FF *B*, resulting in the 1ϕ and $\phi 0$ entries. The minimal equations for J_B and K_B are shown in Figure 9.17*b* as $J_B = A$ and $K_B = \bar{A}$.

This synthesis for the *B* FF can be used for all the FFs just by changing the letters. Thus the *n*th FF is programmed by the 1 and 0 outputs of the $n - 1$ FF, as shown in Figure 9.17*c*. The first FF in the chain is the only FF to see the input data. If the data are 1 the *A* FF must be set to 1; therefore J_A must be 1 while K_A is 0. The logic 0 for K_A is formed by inverting the data line. This also provides the program for the case when the data line is 0, at which time J_A should be 0 and K_A should be 1.

The shift register is a synchronous device because all FFs respond to the input CP, and it requires no additional logic gating, making it the fastest type of sequential logic that can be designed. A 4-bit shift register is shown in Figure 9.17. Its uses include acting as a series-to-parallel converter;

a parallel-to-series converter, in which the FFs are set to predetermined states and the data are shifted out in serial fashion; as a delay line, in which the output from the last register is delayed from the input by the number of bits in the register; and as a ring counter by feeding back the output to the input and presetting the first FF to 1. A five-stage shift register can be used as a BCD counter when properly programmed to sequence the 5-bit, nonweighted code shown in Table 1.6. The shift register becomes a functional building block around which many special-purpose devices are built.

9.6 SPECIAL COUNTERS

Counters that count anything other than a binary multiple are special counters. The BCD counter is a special counter, but is so common that it has been built in a single IC package as a multifunctional device. Counters to count other special numbers are sometimes referred to as modulo counters. A modulo 9 counter is one that has a programmed sequence for nine successive inputs and then repeats itself. It is not very difficult to develop special programming for up to five FFs, but for six and more the synthesis becomes tedious and clumsy. Synchronous counters for counting 2 through 16 with the *J-K* FF are shown in Figures 9.18 through 9.32.

Each figure shows the interconnections required, the equations for each FF, and the sequence of events via a truth table. The counters shown will not lock up in any forbidden state. The equations will allow the reader to revise the implementation to suit a particular logic family. That is, the Sylvania SUHL logic has FFs with three input AND gates as part of the FF, which greatly reduces the number of NAND gates shown here. Variations to the implementations shown are too many to be illustrated, but they must all derive from the synchronous logic and therefore are left to the ingenuity of the reader.

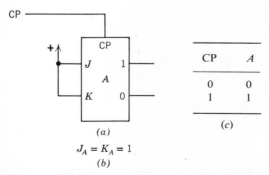

$$J_A = K_A = 1$$
(b)

Figure 9.18 (a) Count-by-2; (b) control equation; (c) truth table.

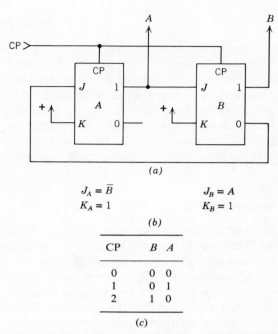

$$J_A = \overline{B} \qquad\qquad J_B = A$$
$$K_A = 1 \qquad\qquad K_B = 1$$

(b)

CP	B	A
0	0	0
1	0	1
2	1	0

(c)

Figure 9.19 (a) Count-by-3; (b) control equations; (c) truth table.

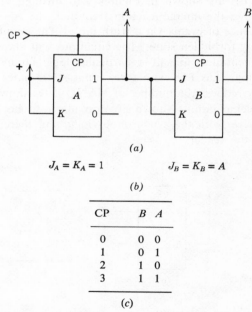

$$J_A = K_A = 1 \qquad\qquad J_B = K_B = A$$

(b)

CP	B	A
0	0	0
1	0	1
2	1	0
3	1	1

(c)

Figure 9.20 (a) Count-by-4; (b) control equations; (c) truth table.

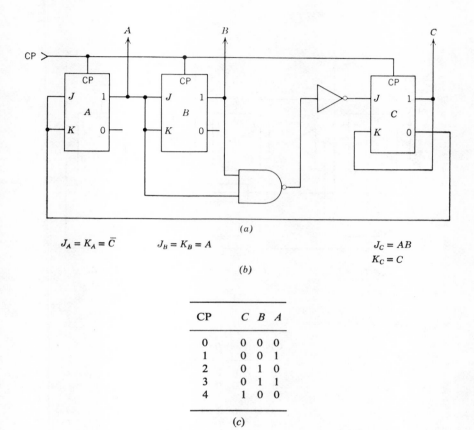

$$J_A = K_A = \overline{C} \qquad J_B = K_B = A \qquad J_C = AB$$
$$K_C = C$$

(b)

CP	C	B	A
0	0	0	0
1	0	0	1
2	0	1	0
3	0	1	1
4	1	0	0

(c)

Figure 9.21 (a) Count-by-5; (b) control equations; (c) truth table.

211

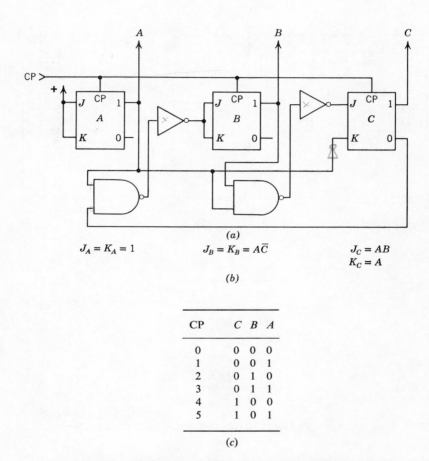

$$J_A = K_A = 1 \qquad\qquad J_B = K_B = A\bar{C} \qquad\qquad J_C = AB$$
$$K_C = A$$

(b)

CP	C	B	A
0	0	0	0
1	0	0	1
2	0	1	0
3	0	1	1
4	1	0	0
5	1	0	1

(c)

Figure 9.22 (a) Count-by-6; (b) control equations; (c) truth table.

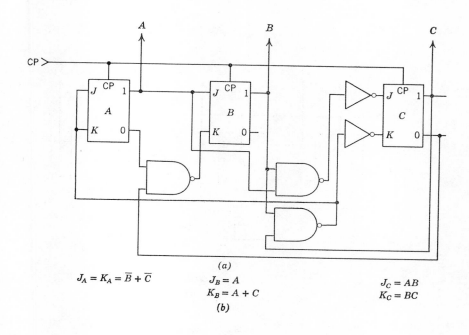

$$J_A = K_A = \overline{B} + \overline{C}$$

$$\begin{array}{l} J_B = A \\ K_B = A + C \end{array}$$

$$\begin{array}{l} J_C = AB \\ K_C = BC \end{array}$$

(b)

CP	C B A
0	0 0 0
1	0 0 1
2	0 1 0
3	0 1 1
4	1 0 0
5	1 0 1
6	1 1 0

(c)

Figure 9.23 (a) Count-by-7; (b) control equations; (c) truth table.

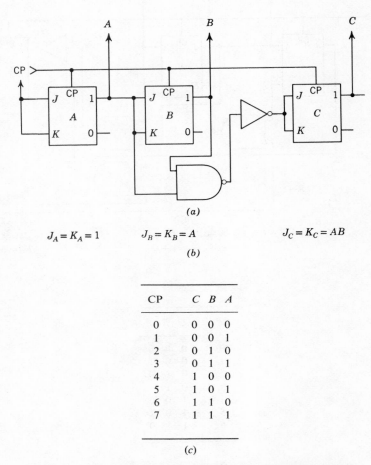

$$J_A = K_A = 1 \qquad J_B = K_B = A \qquad J_C = K_C = AB$$

(b)

CP	C	B	A
0	0	0	0
1	0	0	1
2	0	1	0
3	0	1	1
4	1	0	0
5	1	0	1
6	1	1	0
7	1	1	1

(c)

Figure 9.24 (a) Count-by-8; (b) control equations; (c) truth table.

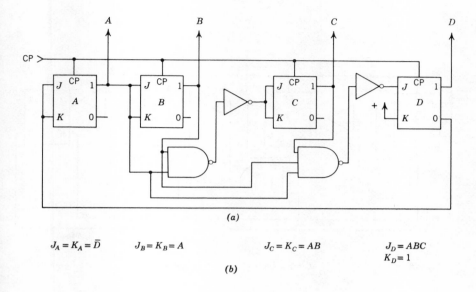

$$J_A = K_A = \bar{D} \qquad J_B = K_B = A \qquad J_C = K_C = AB \qquad J_D = ABC$$
$$K_D = 1$$

(b)

CP	D	C	B	A
0	0	0	0	0
1	0	0	0	1
2	0	0	1	0
3	0	0	1	1
4	0	1	0	0
5	0	1	0	1
6	0	1	1	0
7	0	1	1	1
8	1	0	0	0

(c)

Figure 9.25 (a) Count-by-9; (b) control equations; (c) truth table.

215

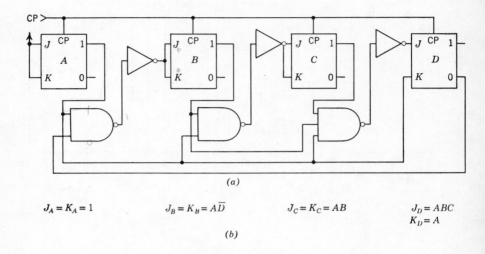

$$J_A = K_A = 1 \qquad\qquad J_B = K_B = A\overline{D} \qquad\qquad J_C = K_C = AB \qquad\qquad \begin{aligned} J_D &= ABC \\ K_D &= A \end{aligned}$$

(b)

CP	D	C	B	A
0	0	0	0	0
1	0	0	0	1
2	0	0	1	0
3	0	0	1	1
4	0	1	0	0
5	0	1	0	1
6	0	1	1	0
7	0	1	1	1
8	1	0	0	0
9	1	0	0	1

(c)

Figure 9.26 (a) Count-by-10; (b) control equations; (c) truth table.

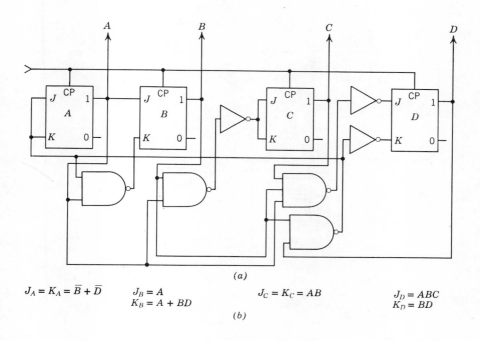

(a)

$J_A = K_A = \overline{B} + \overline{D}$ $J_B = A$ $J_C = K_C = AB$ $J_D = ABC$
                               $K_B = A + BD$ $K_D = BD$

(b)

CP	D	C	B	A
0	0	0	0	0
1	0	0	0	1
2	0	0	1	0
3	0	0	1	1
4	0	1	0	0
5	0	1	0	1
6	0	1	1	0
7	0	1	1	1
8	1	0	0	0
9	1	0	0	1
10	1	0	1	0

(c)

Figure 9.27 (a) Count-by-11; (b) control equations; (c) truth table.

217

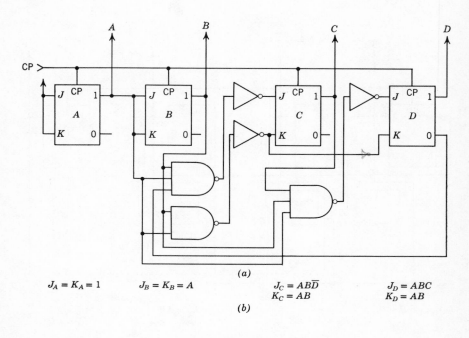

$$J_A = K_A = 1 \qquad J_B = K_B = A \qquad \begin{array}{l} J_C = AB\overline{D} \\ K_C = AB \end{array} \qquad \begin{array}{l} J_D = ABC \\ K_D = AB \end{array}$$

(b)

CP	D	C	B	A
0	0	0	0	0
1	0	0	0	1
2	0	0	1	0
3	0	0	1	1
4	0	1	0	0
5	0	1	0	1
6	0	1	1	0
7	0	1	1	1
8	1	0	0	0
9	1	0	0	1
10	1	0	1	0
11	1	0	1	1

(c)

Figure 9.28 (a) Count-by-12; (b) control equations; (c) truth table.

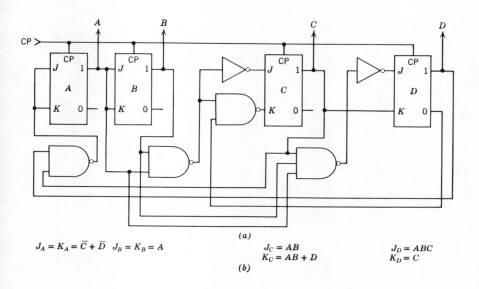

$J_A = K_A = \overline{C} + \overline{D}$ $J_B = K_B = A$

$J_C = AB$
$K_C = AB + D$

$J_D = ABC$
$K_D = C$

(b)

CP	D	C	B	A
0	0	0	0	0
1	0	0	0	1
2	0	0	1	0
3	0	0	1	1
4	0	1	0	0
5	0	1	0	1
6	0	1	1	0
7	0	1	1	1
8	1	0	0	0
9	1	0	0	1
10	1	0	1	0
11	1	0	1	1
12	1	1	0	0

(c)

Figure 9.29 (a) Count-by-13; (b) control equations; (c) truth table.

219

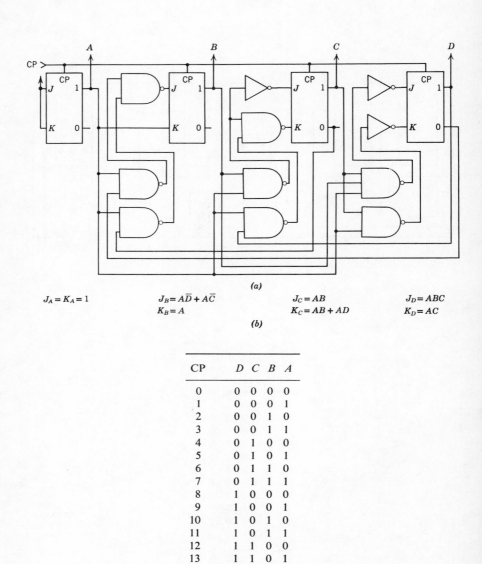

$$J_A = K_A = 1 \qquad\qquad J_B = A\overline{D} + A\overline{C} \qquad\qquad J_C = AB \qquad\qquad J_D = ABC$$
$$K_B = A \qquad\qquad\qquad K_C = AB + AD \qquad\qquad K_D = AC$$

(b)

CP	D	C	B	A
0	0	0	0	0
1	0	0	0	1
2	0	0	1	0
3	0	0	1	1
4	0	1	0	0
5	0	1	0	1
6	0	1	1	0
7	0	1	1	1
8	1	0	0	0
9	1	0	0	1
10	1	0	1	0
11	1	0	1	1
12	1	1	0	0
13	1	1	0	1

(c)

Figure 9.30 (a) Count-by-14; (b) control equations; (c) truth table.

220

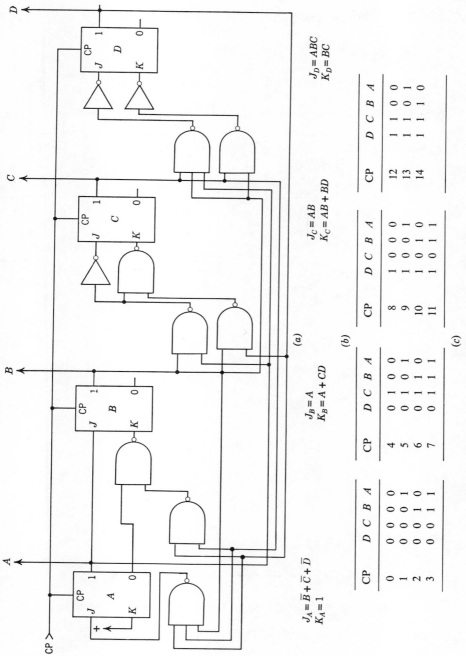

$J_A = \bar{B} + \bar{C} + \bar{D}$
$K_A = 1$

$J_B = A$
$K_B = A + CD$

$J_C = AB$
$K_C = AB + BD$

$J_D = ABC$
$K_D = BC$

(a)

(b)

CP	D C B A		CP	D C B A		CP	D C B A		CP	D C B A
0	0 0 0 0		4	0 1 0 0		8	1 0 0 0		12	1 1 0 0
1	0 0 0 1		5	0 1 0 1		9	1 0 0 1		13	1 1 0 1
2	0 0 1 0		6	0 1 1 0		10	1 0 1 0		14	1 1 1 0
3	0 0 1 1		7	0 1 1 1		11	1 0 1 1			

(c)

Figure 9.31 (a) Count-by-15; (b) control equations; (c) truth table.

221

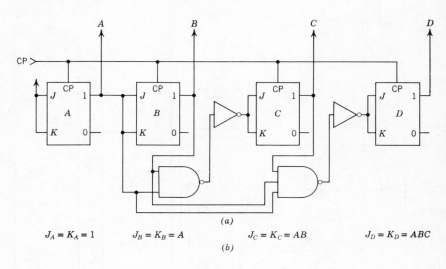

(a)

$$J_A = K_A = 1 \qquad J_B = K_B = A \qquad J_C = K_C = AB \qquad J_D = K_D = ABC$$

(b)

CP	D	C	B	A
0	0	0	0	0
1	0	0	0	1
2	0	0	1	0
3	0	0	1	1
4	0	1	0	0
5	0	1	0	1
6	0	1	1	0
7	0	1	1	1
8	1	0	0	0
9	1	0	0	1
10	1	0	1	0
11	1	0	1	1
12	1	1	0	0
13	1	1	0	1
14	1	1	1	0
15	1	1	1	1

(c)

Figure 9.32 (a) Count-by-16; (b) control equations; (c) truth table.

Counters above 31 are usually made by sensing when the counter reaches the predetermined value and resetting all the FFs to the 0 state on the next CP by appropriate programming. Another approach is to sense when the counter has reached one number less than the desired count and to reset all FFs in the 0 state to the 1 state. This sets the counter to the all-1 state, from which it will automatically return to the all-0 state with the next CP.

PROBLEMS

1. Design and implement a count-by-20 binary counter. Use flip-flop given in Problem 2 below. No preset pulses are available, but starting point is not important. Frequency is not a criterion.

2. Design and implement an up-and-down count-by-5 binary counter using the flip-flop defined by the following characteristic table:

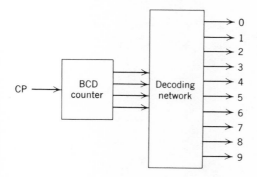

J–K	Flip-Flop
J—K	Q^{n+1}
0 0	Q^n
0 1	0
1 0	1
1 1	$\overline{Q^n}$

3. Given an 8-4-2-1 BCD counter, implement the decoding network for obtaining the 0 through 9 outputs. Use Figure 9.12.

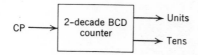

4. Implement a two-decade 8-4-2-1 counter.

5. Given a 10-bit counter, implement a network for an output of 1 whenever the magnitude of the counter is equal to or greater than 0.707 plus 2%, minus zero. The counter represents the magnitude of 0 to 1 with weight assignment as shown.

A	B	C	D	E	F	G	H	I	J

2^{-1} 2^{-10}

10

SPECIAL-PURPOSE
FUNCTIONS

The interconnection of digital building blocks is the main theme of this book. So far it has dealt with individual NAND gates, NOR gates, and flip-flops and the appropriate programming to result in specific functions. Some functions, such as binary counters, are used over and over again and do not need to be continuously developed from basic logic techniques. These functions become special-purpose units, because they perform according to a particular and unique program. A group of FFs interconnected as a binary counter performs as a binary counter and not as a shift register. Four flip-flops interconnected to count as a decade counter can become building blocks for multiple-decade counters. In fact, multifunctional capability in integrated circuits is evidenced by availability of decade counters, full adders, shift registers, decade decoders, multimemory banks, and others in single integrated-circuit packages.

These units are called special-purpose units because they are prewired to perform a special function. This chapter deals with two real-time, special-purpose techniques that have proven quite useful: a discrete multiplier (DM) and a digital differential analyzer (DDA).

10.1 DISCRETE MULTIPLIER

It is common to need a given frequency or CP input reduced by some factor such as 2, 4, 32, or 1024. As long as it is a binary multiple a binary counter of the appropriate length serves very well. That is, a divide-by-4 is accomplished by two FFs connected as a 4-bit counter. To divide a number by something other than a binary multiple, however, is a different problem.

The DM technique accomplishes the reduction of an output frequency by any number between 0 and 1 limited in resolution only by the size of the DM implemented. A 4-bit DM is shown in Figure 10.1. It consists of four J-K FFs programmed as a 4-bit synchronous counter and some additional logic sampling the state of each FF. It should be recalled that whenever the J and K inputs to a J-K FF are high the FF will toggle or change state. Thus the first FF, Q_1, is programmed to change state with every input CP. Q_3 changes state whenever Q_1 and Q_2 are a logic 1, and the fourth FF, Q_4, changes state only when Q_1, Q_2, and Q_3 are 1. These four FFs, then, duplicate a truth table function for 4 bits and act as a binary counter. The counter is synchronous, because any change in the FFs is the result of a common pulse and all FFs change state at the same time.

A timing chart showing the logic level of each of the four FFs is illustrated in Figure 10.2; the width of the CP is assumed to be very short relative to the CP period so that the CP looks like a spike. This is a common way of depicting a CP in a synchronous system. It is seen that after 16 CP inputs the state of the FFs will repeat.

The inputs A, B, C, D, and E to the DM in Figure 10.1 are control inputs. They determine the number of CPs that appear at the output of the network. The frequency of the input CP is called f_1. The frequency of the output

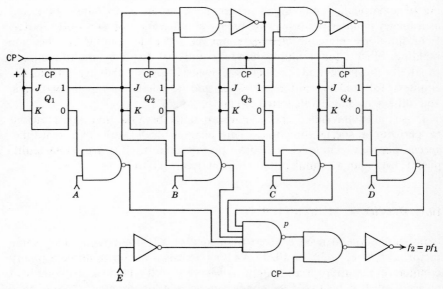

Figure 10.1 Four-bit discrete multiplier.

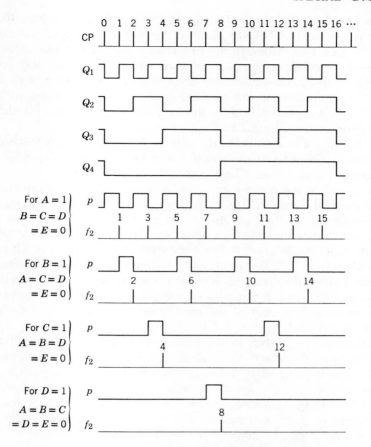

Figure 10.2 Timing chart for 4-bit DM.

CPs is called f_2. The relationship between f_1 and f_2 can be expressed as

$$f_2 = pf_1 \qquad 0 \le p \le 1,$$

where f_1 = input frequency

  p = multiplier

  f_2 = output frequency.

The inputs A, B, C, D, and E are the binary equivalent of the decimal value of the function p. This will become clear as examples are developed.

  The object of the gating network is to sense when each FF is 0 and is going to be set to 1. For FF Q_1, this is true whenever it is 0 because it changes state with each CP. In general a FF is going to be set to 1 when it is in the zero state and its *J-K* inputs are high. Thus in Figure 10.1 the inputs to the control NAND gates are the normal 0 output and the *J-K* input of each FF. Although all FFs change upon command of the CP, an inspection of the timing chart of Figure 10.2 reveals that only one FF undergoes a $0 \rightarrow 1$ transition at any given time. Although many FFs undergo a $1 \rightarrow 0$ transition at various times, only one FF undergoes the $0 \rightarrow 1$ transition with a given CP. It is this fact that is used to achieve the time distribution of the output CPs.

The function p is obtained at the output of the five-input NAND gate of Figure 10.1. The AND'ing of p with the input CP produces a gating of the CPs in such a way that a time-dependent function results.

The results of the control inputs *A*, *B*, *C*, and *D* are illustrated in the timing chart of Figure 10.2. The first set shows the effect of letting input $A = 1$ while inputs *B*, *C*, *D*, and *E* are all 0, thus inhibiting those gates and enabling only the gate with input *A*. The state or logic level of p as a function of time is shown. This logic level serves to gate the CP so that only pulses 1, 3, 5, 7, 9, 11, 13, and 15 appear at the output. This is all the odd-numbered pulses and is exactly one-half of the total number of pulses. For this case it can be said that $p = \frac{1}{2}$ or 2^{-1}. Thus the *A* input serves to control one-half of the input pulses and can be said to have a weight of $\frac{1}{2}$ or 2^{-1}.

The second set of data in the timing chart shows the effect of letting $B = 1$ while *A*, *C*, *D*, and *E* are all 0. This has the effect of sensing when Q_2 is 0 and is going to 1. When this is used to gate the input CP it can be seen that only every fourth CP is permitted to pass, starting with the second CP. Thus, from time zero, pulses 2, 6, 10, 14, 18, 22, 26, and so on are enabled or gated as outputs. This is exactly one-fourth of the input CPs, so that *B* can be assigned a weight of $\frac{1}{4}$ or 2^{-2}.

The third set of data results from $C = 1$ while *A*, *B*, *D*, and *E* are all 0. FF Q_3 goes to 1 only twice in any 16-period count, on command of the 4th and 12th input pulses. Therefore input *C* controls every 8th pulse, starting with the 4th pulse. It would control CPs 4, 12, 20, 28, 36, and so on, of a given input set of pulses. It serves to divide the input by 8, or has a weight of 2^{-3}.

The fourth set of data in the timing chart of Figure 10.2 shows that the *D* input enables only 1 CP in 16. From time zero, therefore, with *D* having a weight of $\frac{1}{16}$ or 2^{-4}, an output is obtained within one-half the time period actually gated. That is, outputs 8, 24, 40, 56, and so on are gated and the number of outputs (at any instant of time) is never wrong by more than one-half the weight of the control inputs. As a frequency synthesizer it can be said that the DM is always accurate within one-half the least significant bit at any instant of time.

The final function, $E = 1$, is not illustrated, as it is self-evident. Because the five-input NAND gate is functioning as an OR gate, if $E = 1$ then $p = 1$ and all input pulses are passed to the output. The other end of the mathematics is for all input controls to be 0; then $p = 0$ and the output is 0.

So far the discussion has developed only values of p that are binary multiples, and this can just as easily be accomplished with the binary counter alone. The object of this game, however, is that by programming the inputs A, B, C, D, and E, any one of 16 different outputs can be obtained from this 4-bit DM. For instance, if $A = 1$ then $p = 0.5$, or if $B = 1$ then $p = 0.25$, but if both A and B are 1 then $p = 0.75$. An inspection of the timing chart shows that if A and B are 1 at the same time while all other inputs are 0 the output consists of pulses 1, 3, 5, 7, 9, 11, 13, and 15 as well as 2, 6, 10, and 14. This is a total of three-fourths of the input, or 12 out of 16 inputs. Thus $p = 0.75$.

Let $B = 1$ and $C = 1$ while A, D, and E are 0. The output will consist of pulses 2, 6, 10, and 14 as well as 4 and 12, for a total of 6 out of 16 or $\frac{3}{8}$ or 0.375, which is the sum of 0.25 and 0.125.

Notice that the decimal 0.375 is equal to 0.011 binary, which is the sum of 2^{-2} and 2^{-3}, which is the weight of the control inputs B and C. It is only necessary to obtain the binary equivalent of the decimal function p to know how the control inputs should be programmed. This will be illustrated by a few examples using the 4-bit DM of Figure 10.1.

EXAMPLE 10.1. *Provide an output equal to five-eighths of the input.*

$$f_2 = \tfrac{5}{8} f_1$$

$$\therefore \quad p = \tfrac{5}{8}$$

$$= 0.625 \text{ decimal}$$

$$= 0.101 \text{ binary.}$$

Therefore $A = 1$, $B = 0$, $C = 1$, $D = 0$, $E = 0$.

EXAMPLE 10.2. *Divide an input frequency by $\tfrac{3}{16}$.*

$$f_2 = \tfrac{3}{16} f_1$$

$$\therefore \quad p = \tfrac{3}{16}$$

$$= 0.1875 \text{ decimal}$$

$$= 0.0011 \text{ binary.}$$

Therefore $A = 0$, $B = 0$, $C = 1$, $D = 1$, $E = 0$.

Note that the input control E has the equivalent weight of $2^0 = 1$.

This 4-bit DM can provide up to 16 different synthesized outputs. These outputs are discrete, as are all binary functions, and are a function of the number of bits. In general, then, an n-bit DM can provide 2^n different synthesized outputs. These outputs are discrete in that they are as accurate as the weight of the least significant bit. The 4-bit DM has a least significant bit weight of 2^{-4}, or $\frac{1}{16}$. Therefore it can provide outputs in multiples of $\frac{1}{16}$. A 10-bit DM can provide 2^{10}, or 1024 different outputs. The output of a 10-bit DM is therefore accurate to 1 part in 1024.

The 4-bit DM illustrated in Figure 10.1 is a general-purpose DM in that it may be programmed by changing the state of the input controls. Quite often a specific function is required for a special application. In this case it would not be necessary to implement all the control functions, just those equivalent control inputs necessary to handle the binary 1's in the binary number.

EXAMPLE 10.3. *Divide a given input frequency by 0.15625.*

The binary equivalent of a decimal number is found by repeated multiplication by 2 as follows:

$$
\begin{array}{rr}
 & 0.15625 \\
 & \times 2 \\
\hline
0.0 & 0.31250 \\
 & \times 2 \\
\hline
0.00 & 0.62500 \\
 & \times 2 \\
\hline
0.001 & 0.25000 \\
 & \times 2 \\
\hline
0.0010 & 0.50000 \\
 & \times 2 \\
\hline
0.00101 & 0.00000
\end{array}
$$

Therefore $p = 0.15625$ decimal

$\qquad = 0.00101$ binary.

The binary number is complete when carried to five places. Therefore a 5-bit DM will provide an exact function with the $0 \rightarrow 1$ transitions of the third and fifth FFs used to gate the input CP. The first, second and fourth FFs must be provided to complete a 5-bit synchronous counter. However, the $0 \rightarrow 1$ translations of the first, second, and fourth FFs are not required for this specific function and need not be implemented. Figure 10.3 shows a 5-bit synchronous counter with the $0 \rightarrow 1$ transitions of the

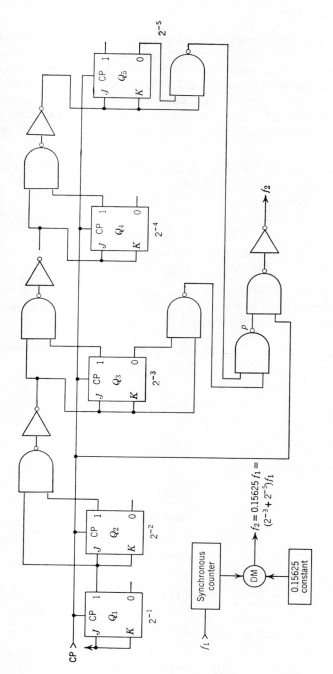

Figure 10.3 Special-purpose DM.

third and fifth FFs sensed and used to gate the input CP. The third FF will enable 2^{-3} or 1 out of 8 or 0.125 of the input pulses, whereas the fifth FF will enable 2^{-5} or 1 of 32 or 0.03125 of the inputs. These two together will provide an output that is 0.15625 times the input. This special-purpose function requires a 5-bit synchronous counter with a hard-wired program, because all $0 \rightarrow 1$ transitions of the third and fifth FFs are required. Thus only two two-input gates are required for programming the output.

EXAMPLE 10.4. A more complicated problem is one in which it is desired to change a frequency or CP input that represents milliradians to one representing degrees. Because there are 2π radians per 360°, there are 17.45 milliradians per degree or

$$f_2 = 1/17.45 f_1.$$

$$\text{Thus} \quad p = 1/17.45$$

$$= 0.057296 \text{ decimal.}$$

Because this is an irrational decimal number it is surely an irrational binary number. Thus a decision must be made as to the degree of accuracy required of the DM. A decimal-to-binary conversion is as follows:

	0.057296
	$\times 2$
0.0	0.114592
	$\times 2$
0.00	0.229184
	$\times 2$
0.000	0.458368
	$\times 2$
0.0000	0.916736
	$\times 2$
0.00001	0.833472
	$\times 2$
0.000011	0.666944
	$\times 2$
0.0000111	0.333888
	$\times 2$
0.00001110	0.667776
	$\times 2$
0.000011101	0.335552

$$\frac{\times 2}{0.0000111010 \quad 0.671104}$$

$$\frac{\times 2}{0.00001110101 \quad 0.342208}$$

Thus $p = 0.057296$ decimal

≈ 0.00001110101 binary (to 11 bits).

But exact conversion to decimal of this 11-bit binary number gives 0.057129, or a decimal error of $\varepsilon = 0.000067$. Thus an 11-bit DM would provide an error of about 0.1%. For purposes of this example it will be assumed that a 7-bit DM is sufficient. The error function in this case is

$$p = 0.0000111 \text{ (binary)}$$
$$= 0.0546875$$

Thus $\varepsilon \approx 0.0026$ or about 4%.

This function is implemented in Figure 10.4, which shows that the only DM NAND gate controls used are on the fifth, sixth, and seventh FFs, as the binary number requires.

EXAMPLE 10.5. So far the examples have dealt with functions where p is a constant. The original DM developed in Figure 10.1 had inputs that could be programmed to provide various outputs as a function of the

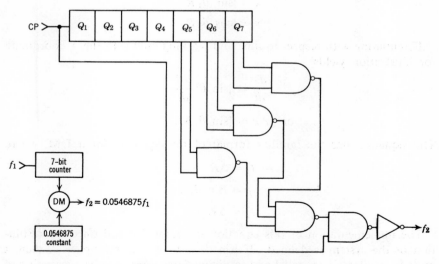

Figure 10.4 Special-purpose DM.

state of the inputs. An example that makes use of this capability is the real-time conversion of radar polar coordinates to Cartesian coordinates. A little explanation will help to clarify this situation.

Assume a ground-based search radar system scanning the air for airborne targets. The radar disk rotates at some fixed rate and at any instant of time is directed at an angle θ relative to North. At regular intervals the radar system radiates a pulse and waits for a return to be reflected from a target. During this waiting period time is counted in fractions of a microsecond, and the amount of time it takes for a transmitted pulse to be reflected by a target back to the radar antenna is a measure of the distance or range of the target. Some specific numbers will be attached to this problem in order to make it a real situation. Assume that the antenna rotational rate is 6 rpm and the pulse repetition frequency (PRF) is 200 cps. Assume that an effective range for the radar is 200 miles. A normal radar-range mile (the amount of time it takes for a radar pulse to propagate 1 mile and return) is 12 μsec. Thus it will take 12 μsec × 200 miles, or 2400 μsec, for the return from a target 200 miles away.

The antenna rotates at 6 rpm or completes one revolution (360°) every 10 sec. It can be said to be rotating at the rate of 36° per sec. The PRF is 200, which results in better than five pulses per degree of rotation. For all practical purposes, therefore, it may be assumed that the antenna is stationary for any given pulse transmission period.

The equation for conversion from R, θ polar coordinates to x, y Cartesian coordinates is

$$x = |\sin \ \theta| \ R$$
$$y = |\cos \ \theta| \ R.$$

Differentiating with respect to time and working only with the X coordinate for illustration yields

$$\frac{dx}{dt} = |\sin \ \theta| \frac{dR}{dt}$$

or $\Delta x = |\sin \ \theta| \Delta R.$

This equation has the familiar format of the equation for a DM, where

$$f_1 = \Delta R$$
$$p = |\sin \ \theta|$$
$$f_2 = \Delta x.$$

The implementation of this equation is straightforward once the resolution of the system is defined. If $|\sin \ \theta|$ is to be the multiplier p, then it must be available in parallel and in digital form. This can be accomplished in several ways, but the easiest to visualize is a 10-bit shaft encoder that provides two sets of 10 output wires each containing the sine and cosine digital magnitudes of the angle. As the antenna rotates, the encoder rotates, and the digital data on each set of the 10 output wires change as a function of the resolution and rate of rotation of the antenna. This provides the digital magnitudes for sin θ and cos θ and becomes the p term in the DM equation.

Since a radar mile is 12 μsec in time, a CP rate of 1.2 μsec will provide a resolution of 0.1 mile. A 10-bit synchronous counter can count 2048 input pulses before it overflows and will therefore handle 2048 × 1.2 μsec or 2457.6 μsec, which is 245.76 miles. This numbers game is not meant to confuse but to illustrate a real-time problem for the DM.

This completes all the essential groundwork. The implementation of the problem makes use of a 10-bit synchronous counter with DM programming exactly as shown in Figure 10.1. The counter, starting at 0, begins to count input pulses at the rate of one every 1.2 μsec every time a radar pulse occurs. It is therefore acting as a range counter, counting pulses representing ΔR. When a return from a target is received the state of this range counter can be sampled to determine actual range to the target. At the same time the digital magnitude of the sine of the azimuth angle θ is applied to the control inputs of the DM gates. It is assumed that this magnitude is constant during one given radar propagation pulse period. The output of the DM is a certain proportion of the input pulses and represents Δx. If these Δx outputs are accumulated in a counter, then the magnitude of x as a function of R and θ is obtained as R goes from 0 to full range and the antenna rotates. Figure 10.5 shows the implementation of this function. The y coordinate is obtained in an identical manner.

It may help to visualize a specific case in which $\theta = 30°$. Sin $30° = 0.5$; therefore the most significant bit of the digital 10-bit sine function must be 1 while all other bits are 0. This most significant bit is wired as the A input

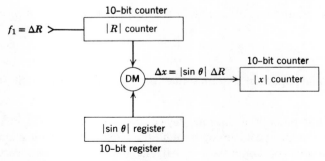

Figure 10.5 Implementation of $\Delta y = |\sin \theta| \Delta R$.

in Figure 10.1, or to the Q_1 FF in the 10-bit range counter. Thus the number of Δx outputs that will occur will be exactly one-half the ΔR inputs. At the same time cos $30° = 0.866$ and the cosine DM inputs contain the binary equivalent of this number, which will result in 0.866 of the ΔR inputs being gated out as the Δy function.

10.2 DIGITAL DIFFERENTIAL ANALYZER

The DDA is another real-time, point-by-point computing technique just as are the binary counter and the DM. In fact it can be shown that the DM is a simplified version of the DDA concept adapted to special applications. The DDA is often referred to as a hard-wired computer; that is, the way in which DDA units are wired and interconnected determines the type of problem being solved. This is opposed to the general-purpose computer, which has computing capabilities as functional blocks, and it is the "softwire," or "program," that determines the type of problem solved. A binary counter is a hard-wired computer in that it is made up of FFs and gates interconnected in such a way that the result is a binary counter. The interconnections of the counter are fixed and solid and cannot be changed by some external program; thus it is a hard-wired unit.

The DDA technique has much the same concept. It is a hard-wired interconnection of counters, adders, accumulators, and timing units that provide a specific solution to a specific problem. It is incremental in nature and provides solutions that are discrete and of finite resolution. A brief explanation of the DDA concept will be given, followed by the implementation of a sine-cosine DDA by way of illustration.

The DDA computes the magnitude of a function by means of successive differential additions. That is, given the function

$$y = Ax,$$

where y is a function of x and A is a constant, differentiation yields

$$dy = A\,dx$$

$$\text{or}\quad \Delta y = A\,\Delta x.$$

A differential equation assumes that Δx approaches the limit 0, so that

$$y = A\int dx.$$

A digital computer is a discrete device and must be limited in resolution to a finite number (Δx cannot be infinitely small) because it cannot do an infinite number of computations. If Δx must be discrete, certainly the smaller it is in magnitude the more accurate will be the result of an integra-

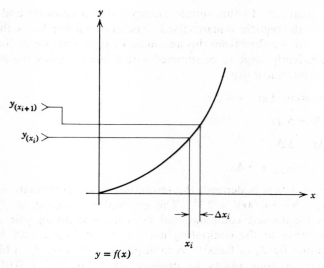

y = f(x)

Figure 10.6 Incremental computation.

tion or summation process. If Δx is discrete and finite, then

$$y_{(x_{i+1})} = y_{(x_i)} + (\Delta y)_{x_i}.$$

Because, from above, $\Delta y = A \Delta x$,

$$y_{(x_{i+1})} = y_{(x_i)} + A(\Delta x_i).$$

This is illustrated in Figure 10.6, where y is some function of x. At some value of x_i of x, y has a value dependent on x_i of $y_{(x_i)}$. If x increases by Δx there will be magnitude Δy, which when added to $y_{(x_i)}$ will give $y_{(x_{i+1})}$. This approach of multiplication and successive addition provides a precise progressive solution that starts with the initial values y_0 and x_0 to arrive at the solution of $y_i = Ax_i$ as x goes from x_0 to x_i in increments of Δx.

The basic parts required to make up a DDA computing unit are the integrating or summation register, the multiplier or full adder, and the accumulator. A binary multiplication is a multiplication by 1 or 0; thus a DDA literally performs a shifting and adding function, storing the results in the accumulator. Summation of successive values of the product term $A \Delta x$ will provide a continuous solution to the described function. The basic computing unit of a DDA is shown in Figure 10.7, where the magnitude of A is

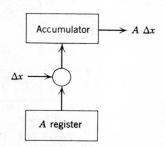

Figure 10.7 DDA computing unit.

stored in a register. In this simple example A is a constant and thus the magnitude of the register remains fixed. The accumulator holds the magnitude $A \, \Delta x$. An overflow from this accumulator represents the Δy increment, which is sufficiently large to be summed with y and increases the magnitude of y by an increment Δy.

EXAMPLE 10.6.   Let $y = 5x$.

Then $dy = 5 \, dx$

   or $\Delta y = 5 \, \Delta x$

and $y_{(x_{i+1})} = y_{(x_i)} + 5 \, \Delta x$.

Once the equation is derived, the resolution of the computation must be defined.   Let $\Delta x = 0.0001 = 2^{-4}$.   This establishes a weight of $\frac{1}{16}$ for Δx and defines the discrete computational steps the computing unit will take. Each pulse input to the computing unit shown in Figure 10.8 represents a multiplication by $\frac{1}{16}$ or 0.0001. A multiplication of 5 by $\frac{1}{16}$ in binary is a decimal shift by four places to produce $(0101) \, (0.0001) = 0.0101$. The magnitude of y after the first x input is thus 0.0101. The second pulse, representing Δx, is again to perform the multiplication of 5 by $\frac{1}{16}$ and add the results to the previous magnitude of y. This second multiplication as well as all multiplications of 5 by Δx will produce 0.0101. Each time a Δx pulse occurs all that is required is to add 0.0101 to the previous sum. This is the function of the accumulator. The accumulator adds the new number to itself and stores the result. Table 10.1 shows the incremental contents of each of the parts of the DDA for 16 Δx inputs. The A register is preset to a magnitude of 5 and is a constant. The accumulator is preset to 0

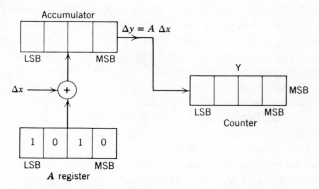

Figure 10.8   DDA computing unit for $\Delta y = 5 \, \Delta x$.

and builds up with each Δx pulse until the summation results in an overflow. These overflows represent increments of Δy, which are summed in the y register so that a running total of the magnitude of y is maintained. The binary numbers shown are arranged as they would appear in the various registers, with the least significant bit to the left.

TABLE 10.1 Magnitudes of Computing Units in DDA

Δx (inputs)	$|A|$	$|A \cdot \Delta x|$	Decimal value	Δy (overflows)	$\Sigma \, \Delta y = y$	Decimal value
	LSB ↓	LSB ↓			LSB ↓	
Preset	1010	0000	0		0000	0
1	1010	1010	5		0000	0
2	1010	0101	10		0000	0
3	1010	1111	15		0000	0
4	1010	0010	4	→	1000	1
5	1010	1001	9		1000	1
6	1010	0111	14		1000	1
7	1010	1100	3	→	0100	2
8	1010	0001	8		0100	2
9	1010	1011	13		0100	2
10	1010	0100	2	→	1100	3
11	1010	1110	7		1100	3
12	1010	0011	12		1100	3
13	1010	1000	1	→	0010	4
14	1010	0110	6		0010	4
15	1010	1101	11		0010	4
16	1010	0000	0	→	1010	5
.	.	.	.		.	.
.	.	.	.		.	.
.	.	.	.		.	.

Because Δx has a magnitude of $\frac{1}{16}$ and $\Delta y = 5 \, \Delta x$, the magnitude of Δy is $\frac{5}{16}$. It stands to reason that the magnitude of y should increase by 5 for every 16 inputs of Δx. The accumulator contains the decimal part of the magnitude of y, so that the actual magnitude of y is determined to 8 bits. For example, after 13 Δx inputs, the magnitude of y should be

$$|y| = (5)(\tfrac{13}{16})$$
$$= 65/16$$
$$= 4.04$$
$$= 0100.0000101$$
$$= 0100.0001 \text{ (to 8 places)}.$$

An examination of the magnitude of the y register and the accumulator after the thirteenth input reveals

$$|y| = 0100$$

$$|Acc| = 0.0001$$

$$|y| + |Acc| = 0100.0001,$$

which is what it should be.

The computation of a sine and cosine function is an interesting problem and will be used to illustrate the effectiveness of the DDA concept.

EXAMPLE 10.7. The sine and cosine digital functions can be computed with two DDA computing units by arranging the equations in a form compatible with DDA techniques.

$$\text{Let} \qquad s = \sin \theta \qquad \text{and} \qquad c = \cos \theta.$$

$$\text{Then} \quad ds = \cos \theta \; d\theta \quad \text{and} \quad dc = -\sin \theta \; d\theta,$$

$$\text{or} \qquad \Delta s = c \; \Delta\theta \qquad \text{and} \qquad \Delta c = -s \; \Delta\theta.$$

Arranging these equations into a DDA format results in

$$s_{(\theta_{n+1})} = s_{\theta_n} + (\Delta s)_{\theta_n}$$
$$= s_{\theta_n} + c(\Delta\theta_n)$$

$$\text{and} \quad c_{(\theta_{n+1})} = c_{\theta_n} + (\Delta c)_{\theta_n}$$
$$= c_{\theta_n} - s(\Delta\theta_n).$$

The two DDA units required to solve the above equations are shown in Figure 10.9. At any given instant in time the contents of the sine register contain the binary magnitude of $\sin \theta$ and the constants of the cosine

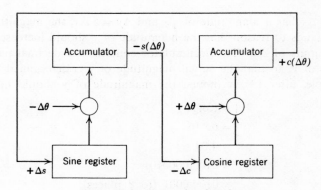

Figure 10.9 Sine-cosine function.

register contain the binary magnitude of cos θ. The only inputs to the unit are a clock pulse representing the magnitude of $\Delta\theta$, a logic level representing the polarity of θ (direction of rotation), and a preset pulse to set up the initial conditions.

Because the sine and cosine registers in Figure 10.9 contain the binary magnitudes of the sine and cosine functions, the number of bits that make up these registers determines the resolution of the sine and cosine functions. The resolution of an n-bit register is 1 part in 2^n. The angle θ must be defined in radians, and therefore the angular resolution in radians is also 1 part in 2^n. It follows that if there are 2^n parts of θ in 1 radian there are $2^n \times 2\pi$ parts of θ in $360°$, or the magnitude of $\Delta\theta$ in degrees is

$$\Delta\theta = \frac{360}{2\pi \times 2^n}.$$

A 10-bit sine-cosine DDA computing unit therefore provides a resolution in magnitude of the sine and cosine of 1 part in 2^{10}, or one part in 1024, and an angular resolution of

$$\Delta\theta = \frac{360}{2\pi \times 2^{10}}$$

$$= 0.056°,$$

which is better than 1 milliradian. This also, of course, determines the number of $\Delta\theta$ input pulses required to complete the computation of the sine and cosine over $360°$ as

$$\Delta\theta \ (\text{pulse per revolution}) = 2\pi \times 2^{10}$$

$$= 2\pi \times 1024$$

$$= 6434.3.$$

Thus the computation of a 10-bit digital sine and cosine function using DDA techniques requires 6434 pulses per revolution, where the incremental pulses represent an angular resolution of $0.056°$ and the sine and cosine are computed to a resolution in magnitude of 0.00098. A 4-bit DDA computing unit will be implemented to compute the sine and cosine functions. It will be assumed that the direction of rotation does not reverse, and therefore the accumulator can be wired to add and need not perform subtraction as well. A $0°$ pulse is assumed available to set up initial conditions. That is, when the $0°$ pulse is received, it will preset the sine register to all 0's (0 magnitude) and the cosine register to all 1's (full magnitude). Figure 10.10 illustrates the magnitude of the sine and cosine registers as the angular function increases from $0°$ to $180°$.

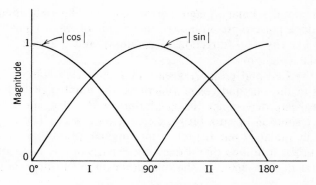

Figure 10.10 Quadrant relationships.

At 0° the magnitude of the sine is 0 and the magnitude of the cosine is 1. As θ increases, the magnitude of the sine increases while the magnitude of the cosine decreases. The rate of change of the sine (around 0°) is very fast, whereas the rate of change of the cosine is slow. Around 90° the reverse is true: the rate of change of the cosine is fast and the rate of change of the sine is slow. At 90° the cosine reaches 0 magnitude and then starts increasing. This is in the second quadrant, and the passage of the cosine register through 0 is sensed in order to change commands to the sine and cosine registers. That is, from 0 to 90°, the sine register adds while the cosine register subtracts in magnitude. After 90° the sine register subtracts while the cosine register adds. This crossover command is developed when the cosine register reaches 0 in magnitude.

A full block diagram of a sine-cosine DDA is illustrated in Figure 10.11, with the polarity control unit serving to keep track of the quadrant and sense 0 magnitudes of the sine and cosine registers. The output of this device is usually the binary state of the sine and cosine registers. These registers are up-and-down binary counters accumulating the overflows of successive additions in the accumulators. An accumulator is made up of full adders and FFs. It stores a binary number and, on command, adds an external number to its own contents and then replaces the old number with the new result. In other words, it adds a number to itself and stores the result of the addition. The overflow from this successive addition increases or decreases the magnitude of the counters representing the sine and cosine functions. The accumulators are initially preset to one-half full magnitude (a 1 in the most significant bit) because it is desired to average the error function.

The implementation shown here represents what may be referred to as a parallel DDA. Extensive work is going on to fabricate a complete DDA

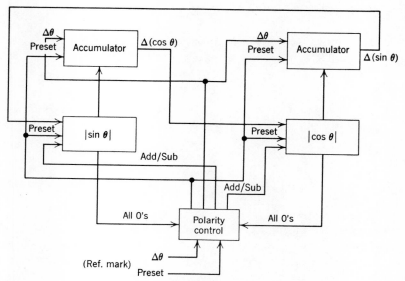

Figure 10.11   Sine-cosine DDA.

computing unit in one monolithic chip by making use of shift registers instead of counters and parallel adders and accumulators. This allows use of **MOS FETS** (monolithic oxide-silicon field-effect transistors) in shift register formats, which can be fabricated in microscopic size.

BIBLIOGRAPHY

Anderson, R. C., R. E. Crippen, and S. M. Fok, "Micrologic System Design Considerations," Fairchild Technical Article, dated June 1962.

Bohn, R., and R. Serds, "Collector Tap Improves Logic Gating," *Electronic Design Magazine*, August 3, 1964.

Boole, G., *An Investigation of the Laws of Thought*, Dover, New York, 1954.

Caldwell, S. H., *Switching Circuits and Logical Design*, Wiley, New York, 1958.

Chua, H. T., "Applications of Milliwatt Micrologic Elements," Fairchild Applications Bulletin APP-64, March 1964.

"Designing with Signetics Integrated Circuits SE 100 Series," Signetics Corp., AN 103, July 1964.

"Graphic Symbols for Logic Design," MIL-STD-806B.

Humphrey, W. S., Jr., *Switching Circuits with Computer Applications*, McGraw-Hill, New York, 1958.

Keelan, R., "Variable Threshold Logic Family of Integrated Circuits," Motorola Application Note AN 200.

Lauders, G. H., "MECL Family of Integrated Circuits," Motorola Application Note AN 201.

Ledley, R. S., *Digital Computer and Control Engineering*, McGraw-Hill, New York, 1960.

Maley, G. A., and J. Earle, *The Logic Design of Transistor Digital Computers*, Prentice-Hall, Englewood Cliffs, N.J., 1963.

Marcus, M. P., *Switching Circuits for Engineers*, Prentice-Hall, Englewood Cliffs, N.J., 1962.

McCluskey, E. J., *Introduction to the Theory of Switching Circuits*, McGraw-Hill, New York, 1965.

Phister, M., *Logical Design of Digital Computers*, Wiley, New York, 1958.

Series 51 Semiconductor Networks Application Report, Texas Instruments, 1962.

"This Is SUHL," Sylvania Folder SM2945.

INDEX